A Journey in Matthew 24

A Theological Novel

Richard P. Belcher

Richbarry Press

105 River Wood Drive, Fort Mill, SC 29715

Phone: 803-396-7962
E-Mail: docbelcher@juno.com • Email: mabelcher@juno.com
Web site: www.richbarrypress.com

Printed in the United States of America

Preface

The book of Matthew, especially chapter 24, is under discussion in our day, more so than it seemed to have been in the twentieth century. The key question today seems to be what to do with Matthew 24, in light of the fact that men are taking that chapter in one of three different ways. Does Matthew 24 speak of the Second Coming of Christ, or does it speak of the Fall of Jerusalem, or does it speak of both the Second Coming and the Fall of Jerusalem?

It seems in the twentieth century more took Matthew 24 to speak of the Second Coming with few seeing it as the fall of Jerusalem. Some have added the idea today that the Second Coming of Christ was at the hour of the Fall of Jerusalem. This is not to say that some of these views were not believed previous to the twentieth century, but it is to state what was taking place in that century.

It is not our desire to speak of these matters by the various names of each view, but it is to set forth very simply our own conviction concerning the subject in this "journey" book. The author realizes his view of Matthew 24 may be somewhat different from many today and of yesterday, but nonetheless he wishes to set forth kindly his ideas in this area of study. He wants to thank all, who have gone before him, and all those who are now writing on the subject of eschatology. Your author is convinced that no area of Biblical doctrine so illustrates the statement of Proverbs 27:17, as does eschatology, as that verse states, *As iron sharpens iron, so one man sharpens another!*

I do thank all of my brothers in Christ for sharpening me, not that I think I have arrived with perfection yet in the area of eschatology or that I have agreed with them. But many have challenged me with their various views again and again down through the years. and I thank you for that, and perhaps this work might do the same for some of you.

Chapter 1

For those of you who have been with us on any of our previous "journeys," I must make it clear that we have never gone out and looked for a "journey" or even anticipated one. They have all brought pressure and danger to us, as men have stood against us, which seems to be the price of standing for the truth. All such events have come unexpectedly, and also at times when I would have been satisfied not to have been challenged by one of them. But of course, Dink[1] and I have learned many spiritual truths and lessons from them, down through the years. So when one of these was over, we rejoiced that God had favored us with such trials, which surely made us better men of God.

So I was not surprised, when I got a phone call one day, which began this present journey, though I could never have anticipated what this journey would involve. The man calling spoke like a British butler of sorts, and he soon informed me that he was calling on behalf of the lady who employed him, and that she had a desire to meet me and a burden to share with me concerning her nephew. She said she would fly me in her private jet to their area in the mountains northwest of me, and she would have her driver meet me at the airport and transport me to her house, so we could talk about a matter, which was very near and dear to her heart. She said she would pay me well for my time and for the ministry she wanted me to give to her nephew.

I must say that she did have something of a mountain brogue, but it was more dignified and refined than most mountain people. She, obviously, had been educated and thus was not like most mountaineers, who were clearly identified by their speech pattern. This is not a critique of the way mountain folk talk, for I had to admit that I loved their brogue and the way they pronounced their words with something of a drawl. Plus, most of them were a people with a sincerity and simplicity that one does not find in many other places.

After asking a few more questions and really not getting many answers, I learned enough that I decided that I would seek to help her on one condition---if I could bring with me my right hand man, Dink. After hearing about Dink and his background, she said that she would be very excited to meet both of us. And so a date was set, as to when we would fly up one day and fly home the next day, due to our schedule.

Thus, in a few days Dink and I were off to the airport, and sure enough, when we got there, we found a Learjet waiting for us to transport us to meet our new found friend and help her with her problem. Dink, however, was a little apprehensive, wondering if someone was setting us up for something, for in a number of our "journeys" that had been the case. I assured him that I had done some research on this woman, a Mrs. Arbella Cardieux, and she was a very wealthy person---I mean a very wealthy person! Obviously, again, that was not the reason we were going to try to help her, but this just seemed to be someone who needed help and was sent by the Lord to us---at least she sounded that way on the telephone. And maybe we could help her and minister to her and her nephew, whatever his problem and need might be.

I must admit, as we flew over the mountains, where we were to land soon. I couldn't see from above, as we came down out of the clouds, much more than the mountains. But then, sure enough there was a runway awaiting us in a clearing of sorts, and we swooped down and made a normal landing, like we were in an area of the flatlands. One needs only a proper stretch of ground, which can look like a postage stamp from the sky, to land safely, once one is close enough to see the proper length of the runway.

When the plane landed, a very luxurious limousine was there to take us to Mrs. Cardieux's home, and what a house it was---the biggest house I have ever seen, located on a giant plot of land, which was separate from any of the other houses in the area. She met us at the door, as we came up to this mansion, and she heartily greeted us and expressed her deep thanks that we had come. We were shown to our rooms and instructed to be ready for supper at 6:00 PM. Until then we could rest and refresh ourselves and even use the indoor swimming pool, if we wished. I wanted to ask her something about her nephew, and how she wanted us to help him, but I did not get the opportunity at this time.

I could hardly wait till supper, as I rested on my soft bed, not because of the meal, though I was certain it would be a feast. I wanted to learn more about her nephew and what we could do to help him.

---

1. Dink is Ira Pointer's companion in all the "journey" books, except the first one. He is a former gang member and was moving up in the Mafia, and he was even in line for possible leadership of a gang movement called "The Almondine!" But because of Ira Pointer's witness to him, he was saved in the unfolding of the plot of the second "journey" book, *A Journey in Purity*. As Pastor Ira Pointer then faced some very dangerous situations in the various "journey" books, Dink stands with him, after he is saved, and he becomes a special friend, who is in every "journey" book thereafter, except for the one journey book, *A Journey in Christian Heritage*, which is a true story of the heritage of your author.

Chapter 2

When we did finally gather for supper, the first part of our time together was spent in getting acquainted. After telling Mrs. Cardieux of our past history, we then found out something of her life and history. She had grown up dirt poor in the hills and mountains of this area, but she became quite wealthy in the area of fashion design and women's clothing. She also had married into wealth, after she had made a fortune in her fashion ventures. Unfortunately, she told us with a tear in her eye, that her husband had died at a young age in a car wreck, and she had remained single ever since.

She was quite fascinated with Dink's story of having been a rising member of that mafia group, when God saved him. And she was also interested in my background, as I was reared as an orphan and had not found my mother and father till I was grown. Finally, after getting acquainted, we came to the reason she had contacted me.

She told us of her nephew, Billy Hill, who was quite a boy, as he was a very popular preacher among the mountain people. He had two uncles, Mrs. Cardieux's brothers, who had begun promoting him in his preaching ministry, when he was in his early teens. It seems God had gifted him with an unusual ability to communicate the gospel with these mountain folk in a very humble and powerful way. But over the years, because Billy's parents were dead, his two uncles, Mrs. Cardieux's brothers, had been getting most of his money from his ministry, for being his "promoters." They called him "Billy Hill---the Hillbilly Preacher!" But, Billy, being a very shy and simple boy, except when he got in the pulpit and cut loose with his sermon, had not and could not stand up to his uncles concerning their keeping most of the money of his ministry. Mrs. Cardieux had even talked to them, but they ignored her, and Billy was now fearful to face his uncles with what they were doing. Mrs.

Cardieux had even then accused them of cheating Billy, but they told her to shut up and mind her own business.

Billy had privately talked to Mrs. Cardieux about the matter, and the brothers had found out and that had made the brothers furious, and they even threatened Billy with severe punishment, if he ever did such a thing again. Her burden was not only to get Billy out from under the influence of her brothers, but also that as he would leave her brothers, someone would teach him more about the Bible and the content of his sermons. Billy's delivery was tremendous, and people were being saved, but she longed for someone to teach him how he could put more depth in his sermons, while keeping his humility and ability to reach the mountain folks. And that is why she had called us.

How's that for an assignment? Not only to help a young preacher, but to do it in the midst of two mountaineer uncles, who in a context of uncertainty, would feel threatened financially, and who knows what their reaction might be to that possibility? But will Billy even be brave enough to try to separate from his uncles? I asked her if she had spoken to Billy about the matter, and she said she had, and he was willing to meet with us for study, whatever the brothers might say or do, which kind of left us in the middle of it all.

When our discussion was over, she gave me a $5000 check, which almost shocked the life out of me, and she said that was just the beginning! She acknowledged that it might take some time to break the the hold of her brothers on Billy, which didn't encourage us any. But when Dink and I had talked about it alone for awhile and prayed about the matter, we felt led of the Lord to seek to help Mrs. Cardieux and Billy. She said she would mention us to Billy soon, and she was sure Billy would be eager to meet with us, if it meant the opportunity to study the Word of God.

5

I told her I would also like to go and hear Billy preach sometime soon, and she said he was preaching in this area this week, and we could go to his services tomorrow night, if we were able to stay over for one more day, which we decided to do. I was eager to get some idea of his preaching, and note the strong points, as well as his weak points, which probably would be the content of his sermon. So we would suffer one more day for Jesus in this massive mansion, but to be honest it seemed lonely and foreboding in many ways.

I wondered as I went back to our comfortable rooms in this massive house, if I could ever live in such a place. It seemed so lonely and desolate. I was not thinking of the mountain area, but the overwhelming size of the house of Mrs. Cardieux, though the area itself was not inviting to me either. It appeared to be not only a lonely house, but it was also in a cold and barren place in the mountains. I concluded that I might be happier in my own house, or even a house the size of some of the mountain folks, instead of this big house. The mountain area, though, would always be a block to ever moving there, which I had no intention of doing---unless God called me there.

But my heart went out to these people, and so I stopped and prayed for them, even for Billy's uncles. I prayed also that God would let us---Dink and me---somehow to have an impact on the whole of this mountain community, though I had no idea how that could ever be. How could we ever communicate with this culture or gain their respect? They, no doubt, thought we were stuck-up city folks, and with the word "doctor" on our names, that might even make it worse! But the Lord had sent us here, and I prayed we could help not only Billy, but his uncles and the whole mountain area, though again, I had no plan or idea of how all of that might ever come to pass.

Chapter 3

The next evening found us driving ourselves in Mrs. Cardieux's cheaper automobile and not her fancy limousine, for that would have been too obvious and maybe even leave the wrong impression on the mountain folk. So by ourselves and with her directions, we made our way through the mountains, way back into the innermost parts of creation, passing ram-shackled houses and people, who looked like real "hillbillies" (at least to us). They were in their yards, and they were sitting on their porches, even with their hound dogs. Some were even working on their cars, which were jacked up in one manner or another. This was clearly a culture of mountain people, and if there was a church to be found, it too would obviously be filled with such people. Not that I minded or had any prejudice against mountain folks, but this was a culture I had only heard about or read about. I had never been in the midst of such a culture with such an obvious poverty. I had seen poor folks, but not like these.

Finally we came to a church, which was backed up to a mountain, and one could tell by the vehicles that even our automobile was out of place, as most cars in the parking lot were older and run-down species from a few decades past. Obviously, Mrs. Cardieux was not with us, for that would have given us away, also, and even more so. This way they might wonder who we were, but would not know for sure.

As we got out of our car, most of the people just stood and stared at us, perhaps shocked to see us there. And I must admit, compared to how they dressed, we were over-dressed for the occasion, something we had missed in our plans to remain almost invisible. So Dink and I made our way into the church and found some empty seats in the back of the building, and finally some of the people began to welcome us. And up close one could tell the reality of their mountain existence, for their faces looked hardened, but even through such faces, they smiled at us, but most did not quite know what to say nor how to greet us.

Finally, a piano player began to play, and could she ever play the piano! There was some jazziness in her soul, which came out in the songs, and the people sang them in the same manner, some even stomping their feet, while they clapped their hands along with some "Amens!" thrown in throughout the song. I took this to mean they were emphasizing the words of the song, as they sang them. This went on for about an hour or so with several special music numbers interspersed. The solos were even in their brogue, and at times they were a little flat and squeaky and squawky.

But one could not doubt the sincerity and spirited emotion, which was in their hearts, as they sang and exalted our Lord. To be honest, they had more depth of emotion and meaning in what they sang than many "uptown" churches I had preached in.

Finally, "Billy Hill---the Hillbilly Preacher"---as Billy was called---was introduced, and he took the pulpit and began his sermon. He was preaching this evening on Matthew 24, and as the message unfolded, he applied all of that chapter to the second coming of Christ, totally overlooking the context of the passage and Matthew's gospel. Billy himself was a very humble young man in the pulpit, but he also evidenced a definite conviction, that he believed what he was preaching was the truth of God. He did have some strange pronunciations, as "Jesus" became "Jeeeeesus" and "loves" became "loooooooves" and "me" became "meeeeee!" "He" became "Heeeeee" and the same with "is my Savior!" I think you get the idea! And at the end of almost every sentence, the congregation erupted with "Amens" almost in unison. Some even responded by getting up and taking a little dance around the church, as

Billy continued preaching, louder at times, which might cause one to think he was going to blast out our ear drums, and softer at other times, when he could barely be heard.

By the end of the service, almost the whole congregation (except Dink and I) was dancing and shouting and rejoicing, and I wondered if they were going to bring out some snakes, so we would see an example of snake-handling also. But I concluded after awhile, that they were not snake-handlers, which was a positive, as far as I was concerned.

We didn't get to meet "Billy Hill---the Hillbilly Preacher" personally, because as the service was letting up a little in its excitement, but still going strong, Dink and I left, not wanting to have to face the uncles, who we had identified, as being the ones sitting on the front row of the church. They were dressed to the hilt, and it was obvious that they were over-dressed for this crowd, also. It was clear Billy's preaching had put them into the snazziest of clothing, along with other non-spiritual benefits.

We arrived back at Mrs. Cardieux's home about 11:00 PM, and when we met her in her large living room, she had a surprise for us. Billy had called her just a few minutes ago, and he wanted to know if she had sent us to the services, and if she had, he wanted to know who we were. When she told him we were seminary professors, he wanted to know if he could see us tonight.

When she told Billy that we had to leave early the next morning, he said he would come this evening, almost begging to be able to do so. So she told him to come on, and then she apologized to us and hoped we would not mind what she had done. When I asked how he would get away from his uncles, she said he was an expert at doing that, though sometimes it took him a little while to do so. And so we waited till well past midnight, and when Billy finally came through the door, he was apologizing to us concerning his inability to ditch his uncles any sooner. We told him not to worry about it. Mrs. Cardieux told us to go ahead and get acquainted with Billy, And then she smiled, as she said, "You men talk, and I will take care of my brothers, if they arrive. They have messed up Billy's life in the past---but not tonight, and hopefully for the last time!"

But then before Mrs Cardieux could get to the front door to guard it and head off the brothers, here they came uninvited through the front door and on back to the place where we were meeting. Obviously, being brothers to Mrs. Cardieux, they didn't stop to knock, but burst in boldly and began to berate Billy and Mrs Cardieux and Dink and me as well, for tampering with Billy and his success as a preacher. And they guaranteed us, they would put a stop to our intrusion into their business.

I was somewhat fearful that they might begin a fight, fearful not for us, but for them, because Dink would clean their plow good, if they did such a thing. But about that time, the police arrived, for it seems the British butler had called them when the brothers came barging through the front door uninvited. But then I thought the brothers might even try to take on the police, too, in their fit of rage. But then, probably recognizing the seriousness of that idea, they soon left, but not without some shouting and cursing, as they were escorted by the police out the front door.

It was obvious they were not going to turn loose of Billy without a fight, which gave rise to some concern on my part. How far would they go in guarding Billy, their prized possession? Were they capable of the murder of their enemies, if they thought they were going to lose Billy and the income he was bringing in, which was going straight into their pockets?

I began to wonder what Dink and I had gotten into!

Chapter 4

As I turned from the exiting brothers, I noticed that Billy was shaking, and he certainly seemed very frightened at what he wanted to do---break loose from his uncles and find help in his preaching ministry. And it was obvious, also, that his uncles were still in his mind, as they overshadowed our whole meeting with him. I will not try to quote him, evidencing his mountain brogue, but if the reader will remember from the last chapter, he spoke softly and gently and graciously, but not at this hour, Now he spoke with a frightened voice and manner, but at least he was trying to communicate with us.

He first thanked us for coming to his services and also for our desire to help him, and he stated clearly that he knew he needed help---not only to get away from his uncles, but also to learn more of how to preach and handle the truth of the Bible. It seems this had bothered him for a number of years, and he had tried before to break loose from his uncles and get an education. But they told him an education would ruin him, and he would then no longer be able to communicate with the mountain people.

And then he asked me a very difficult question. He wanted me to give him an honest opinion of his sermon that I had heard that evening. I was glad that my teaching of preaching had taught me to dwell on the positives of a sermon, when a student had preached in class, and then mention the negatives and the areas in which he needed improvement. So I complimented his delivery, which was unique, but yet it communicated with the people. They heard him clearly and understood what he said, and that is a necessity that every preacher needs to learn, if he is going to communicate with people. There is no excuse or reason for a man to preach in a dull and dry manner---his heart and emotions and feelings must be in the sermon, not in some false manner, but in a real way, whereby the people can see and know that what he says is the truth, or at least that the preacher believes what he is preaching is the truth.

After discussing his excellent delivery for awhile, I turned to his content---the content of his sermon---and here I asked him some basic questions. Could he tell me the historical context of Matthew 24? Could he tell me the context of the book of Matthew, which led up to chapter 24? Did he understand how the entire context of Matthew and the other gospels related to the Old Testament? Trying to answer these questions, he fell flat on his face. It had never dawned upon him to consider such things in his handling of a verse or section of Scripture. It was as if he thought a verse or passage stood by itself, and nothing else mattered in the exegesis of Scripture. Understandably, he didn't know what it meant to exegete Scripture either.

He had been accustomed to reading "good-old-boy" sermons, which had been published in various preachers' magazines or papers. These men took a verse which was printed at the beginning of the sermon, and little was said about the verse or context or word meanings the rest of the message. The verse or verses were just a diving board to allow them to do some daring black flips and somersaults into some popular theme or subject of the day, setting forth some shallow or false sensational thoughts, which would cause the folks listening to say when he was finished, "Oh, that was so deep!!! That was real preaching!!!" All the time it was just some tom-foolery to impress the people with little or no depth of truth to it at all.

As I explained these matters to him, he sat with a dumbfounded look on his face, but he was shaking his head in agreement with what I was saying. I felt sorry for him. Here sat a young man, who was a very humble person, who had been doing his best to preach, who had been hailed as a great and powerful preacher, who had been accepted by the mountain folk, who had been promoted highly to where he had a gigantic following all over the the mountain area. And yet he had come to understand that something was missing in his ministry, even though he was heralded by all as a great preacher. And God had brought him to us---Dink and me---to help him grow and develop in his preaching ministry.

It was about this time that his uncles showed up again, as they broke down the front door. They said they had come back to get Billy now, since the police were gone. As they made a move towards Billy, they told him they were going to take him home, but Dink stepped forward and graciously told them to stop, and if they did not leave, they would be forced to leave.

They did stop, but only so they could sarcastically say, "Yeah, and whose gonna make us stop now? You ain't got any police now!" And when they made another step, Dink floored both of them! Good old Dink! The former gangster, who wasn't very big, but I had seen him take out men twice his size and sometimes even two such men---as he did now! As they sat dazed on the floor, Dink and Mrs. Cardieux gave them an ultimatum---get out and never come back--- and leave Billy Hill alone. From now on they would no longer be his managers.

As they got up and were leaving, they promised there would be no more preaching opportunities for Billy. They would make sure of that. They would shut down his ministry, which meant canceling all his future preaching dates, and they said he was booked for two years. They warned that he would come crawling back to them, begging for their help, because when they got done with him, his ministry would be over---forever!

After they were gone, Billy broke down and cried---he was a tender-hearted boy. He said he knew this hour had to come, but like many instances in life, breaking up with friends or loved ones, even when they have done you wrong, can be a such a sorrowful moment. I moved over and prayed for him, remembering some of my past broken friendships and how heartbroken they had left me.

As I went to bed that night, I couldn't help but recall what I had prayed earlier in that day---that God would open the hearts of the mountain people to the gospel and to Dink and myself. It seems, however, that we had just ruined that possibility, when Dink had decked Billy's two uncles, for there was no telling how they would relay that to the mountain people. We would be pictured as the worst of the worst---preachers who had beaten up two men of their area. We probably would also be painted as the ones who split up Billy and his uncles, because we wanted to get to the money that Billy took in, which was absolutely false.

It would be the educated and uppity-uppity city boys against the mountain folks! It would be Mrs. Cardieux and her friends (us) against the poor folks, because as wealthy as she was, she probably was misunderstood in the community also! It would be the educated (men with doctorates) against the uneducated (the simple mountain people)! It would be the hard-working common folks against the cushy and comfortable preachers, who had little knowledge of the hardships and difficulties of being poor mountain people! It might take a few days to get into the paper, but if I was a betting man, the clash between Billy and his brothers, would soon make the front page of the local paper, with Mrs. Cardieux and us being blamed for the split between Billy and his brothers.

Now how could the Lord ever answer my prayer that Dink and I might make a spiritual impact on the mountain folks of this area? Villains make poor witnesses for Christ, even though their villanization by their enemies was false!

Chapter 5

In the days which followed Mrs. Cardieux was able to contact most of the churches, where Billy was scheduled to preach, and they all, after hearing her explanation of the situation, kept Billy booked as a speaker in their church for the already scheduled dates. It was agreeable with us, also, that on Saturdays Dink and I would be flown by one of Mrs. Cardieux's Learjets to the area where Billy was speaking, so I could teach him more about preaching and how to handle the Word of God. And our first concern was to teach him the importance of the context of a passage.

So the first time we gathered for study, I asked him to explain to me why he thought Matthew 24 spoke of the Second Coming of Christ. His explanation was very clear, as he gave me the following reasons.

1. Because Jesus' disciples asked Him in verse 3 what would be the sign of His coming, Billy thought it must be speaking of the Second Coming of Christ!

2. Billy then said that in the following verses Jesus gave His disciples and us warnings concerning His Second Coming! 4-14
   > Don't let any man deceive you about the SC! 4
   > Many will claim to be Christ and deceive many! 5
   > There will be wars and rumors of wars! 6
   > Do not allow such to trouble you! 6
   > All these things must come before the end comes! 6
   > Nation shall rise against nation! 7
   > Kingdom shall rise against kingdom! 7
   > There will be famines and pestilences and earthquakes in various places! 7
   > All these are the beginning of sorrows! 8
   > Then men will be delivered up to be afflicted! 9
   > Believers will be killed & hated for Christ's sake! 9

We will be hated by all nations for His namesake! 9
Many will betray and hate one another! 10
Many false prophets will arise & deceive many! 11
Many will grow cold because of much iniquity! 12
The one enduring to the end will be saved! 13
This gospel will be preached in all the world 14
    to all nations and then the end will come!

3. Another sign is given for them to understand that His
Second Coming is near! 15-20
When they see the abomination as spoken by 15
    Daniel the prophet they are to do the following--
        they must flee to the mountains! 16
        he on the house top takes nothing with him! 17
        he in the field---goes not back to the house! 18
        woe to those with child! 19
        woe to those nursing children! 19
        pray your flight will not be in the winter! 20
        pray your flight will not be on the Sabbath! 20

4. A great tribulation is coming at this time! 21-31
    this will be such a tribulation not seen since the
        world began! 21
    except those days of tribulation be shortened
        before His coming---no flesh shall be saved---
            but for the elect's sake---those days
                will be shortened! 22
    if one says Christ is in a certain place---
        believe it not! 23
    there will be false Christs and false prophets who
        show great signs and wonders---that if it were
            possible they would deceive the elect! 24
    if they say---He is in the desert or He is in the
        secret chambers---He is not there! 26

as the lightening comes out of the east and shines
    to the west--so will be the SC! 27
immediately after this tribulation---29
    the sun will be darkened!
    the moon shall not give its light!
    the stars shall fall from the heavens!
    the powers of the heavens shall be shaken!
and then shall appear the sign of the Son of man
    in the heavens and then shall all tribes of the
        earth mourn and they shall see the Son
            of man coming in the clouds of heaven
                with power and great glory! 30
and He shall send His angels and they shall 31
    gather His elect from the four winds from one
        end of heaven to the other!

5.   The parable of the fig tree! 32-35
        when the fig tree's branches are tender and puts
            forth leaves---you know that summer is near! 32
        likewise when you shall see all these things you will
            know that the SC is near--even at the door! 33
        verily I say unto you, This generation shall not
            pass till all these things be fulfilled! 34
        heaven and earth shall pass away but my words
            shall not pass away! 35

6.   Further Enlightenment concerning the SC 36-51
        no man knows the day nor hour of the SC! 36
        it will be like the days of Noah---unexpected 37-39
        two will be in the field---one taken--one left! 40
        two women grinding at mill--one taken--one left! 41
        watch---you don't know when He is coming! 42
        householder didn't watch---house vandalized! 43
        be ready---He is coming in hour you think not! 44

blessed is a busy servant when the Lord comes! 46
the faithful servant will be rewarded! 47
an evil servant says the Lord delays His coming! 48
an evil servant lives wickedly when Lord comes! 49
the Lord comes in a day when men think not! 50
such men will be given a portion of the hypocrite
   ---a place of weeping and gnashing of teeth! 51

I thanked Billy for his presentation, and then I asked him one question---Do you see any of these verses giving a warning of the coming of the fall of Jerusalem in the days of Christ's disciples in 70 AD? He looked back at me puzzled, as if he had not seen or thought of or ever heard of an event or idea, such as the fall of Jerusalem. And maybe it was true that he didn't even know that Jerusalem had fallen in 70 AD and was dormant for years and years. I told him his assignment for the next week was to read this chapter again carefully and see if there is any hint of the fall of Jerusalem. And then go and read Josephus concerning the fact that Jerusalem did fall in 70 AD and what events did take place at that hour. Then, also, read carefully the entire book of Matthew and see if there is any hint of Christ rejecting His people, because they have rejected Him. Is there any mention of the fall of Jerusalem, which even His disciples may have missed in this context?

When we parted, Billy was quite excited, and he promised me he would do as I asked for our next meeting. We said our good-byes, and we made our way to the local airport for the ride home in the Learjet, and believe it or not, I actually took a nap as we flew through the skies. I could hardly wait for next Saturday, not just for the jet ride, but most of all for the opportunity to help a very sincere young man, who had been short-changed concerning his ministerial training because of two uncles.

Chapter 6

It was the middle of the next week when I got a visit from the uncles in person, and they brought their lawyer with them---at least that's who they said he was. They presented me with a document of sorts---several misspelled words, and surely not the kind of document one would expect from a regular lawyer. It seemed more like a home-made job that they had done themselves and then enlisted a friend to come, claiming he was their lawyer! They did most of the talking, as the lawyer just sat silent.

The document they showed me said they had made a contract with Billy Hill to be his manager, and they would also have sole control over his ministry, as to when and where he spoke and over the distribution of the funds, which came in from his ministry. They even called their relation to him a "corporation," and the two of them were the sole authorities, and Billy was to be under their control in this ministry, as long as they so desired. It was signed and stamped and did appear to be somewhat legitimate, except it seemed rather amateurish. But maybe that was the way they did it in the mountains, where they were from.

But there was one thing missing---a phone number, whereby I could call an office to verify the reality of their document and supposed lawyer. When I asked for a phone number, they blushed, and said that it would do no good to call the lawyer's office, because he was with them and did not have any one working for him. I asked for the number, anyway, so I could call and get an answering machine, and they responded that he didn't have an answering machine. And when I asked their so-called lawyer, he seemed confused, not knowing what he was supposed to say, and then he agreed with them, as they told him what to say.

I then asked for the phone number of their county's court house, where such documents were recorded, and again they turned several shades of red, and told me their county didn't have such a thing as a court house. I then asked them for the name of the county where they lived, and again I got nothing but false impossible answers, such as, they didn't remember the name of their county!

Thus, it was obvious---they had no such legal document, and what I held in my hand was a fake. I told them that I was going to call the authorities in their county and send this fake document to said authorities, suing the two of them and their false lawyer for false legal practices and for false claims for him to be a lawyer. Then when I told them how many years they could get in jail for such actions, they seemed scared half to death, and they finally confessed that it was not a legal document, and then they begged me to give it back to them, which I refused to do.

I assured them I would keep this document, and if they ever interfered with Billy and his ministry and his desire to go deeper in the Word of God, that I would use this document against them. When I asked them if they understood, they eagerly said they did, and that I would never hear from them again. And out the door and down the road they went in their fancy, shiny, new car, which surely was one of their perks and benefits of handling Billy and his ministry. What scoundrels!

I wondered if we had seen the last of them, but then I realized there were many ways they might try to get at Billy or me indirectly, whereby they would do their dirty work unseen and behind the scenes. My mind began to wonder what their next move might be, for I was certain they would not be easily convinced to give up their high life style without a further fight. It seemed to me that the battle had just begun. But we had won the first several skirmishes. The real war, however, was still in front of us. I began to sing, Faith mighty faith, the promise sees, and looks to God alone.

Chapter 7

A week had passed by the time Billy and I met again at his aunt's home for study. In our first session I had asked Billy to tell me the meaning of Matthew 24, and he had given an understanding that this section of Scripture spoke primarily and only of the Second Coming of Christ. Now I asked him if he had this past week considered the context of this chapter in the Bible? I shouldn't have been surprised at his answer, when he told me he didn't know what I meant by "context!" I told him that in studying the Bible "Context is king," and we must never forget that. I further explained my statement by telling him that in order to understand any passage or section of Scripture, we needed to take into consideration the surrounding passages and events, which might give us light on the meaning of the text we were studying. That is how we consider the "context."

Further, we needed to understand that the context of a passage or verse might be immediate or remote and perhaps even include the extended remote events or passages in the Bible. For example, Matthew 24 has the remote context of the entire Biblical history of the Jews in the Old Testament, for they were the chosen people of God, but through their history, they were not the obedient people of God, as they continually drifted from God and His truth. Few men, after the fall of man in Genesis, were faithful to God, even during the days of Abraham and his family in Genesis, when God had called Abraham and his people to be His own. Then, when God sent them down into Egypt through Joseph to grow into a great nation, they were certainly influenced by the pagan Egyptians. So much so, that when Moses was sent to lead them out of Egypt, they liked that idea, mainly because they had become slaves. But when the hour came, and Moses led them out in the midst of God's power and miracles, they fought Moses all the way. At the Red Sea they had little or no faith. On their way to Mount

Sinai and while there, they grumbled and complained against God and Moses and wanted to go back to Egypt. Time and again, as they journeyed towards the promised land, they rebelled against God and Moses, and finally, when the hour came to go in and take the land, they listened to the ten negative unbelieving spies they had sent to spy out the land, and these spies scared the people into refusing to go in to conquer the land. Thus, they wandered in the wilderness because of their UNBELIEF, for forty years, till all those who were twenty years of age and upward had died in the wilderness, which was their punishment for their UNBELIEF. (Numbers 14:29)

When the younger generation, which had been spared death, came out of the wilderness forty years later, they seemed to have been a more godly people, who desired to honor God and obey their leaders. And so God honored their faith, though along the way they did make a few mistakes---such as an over-confidence following their absolute victory over Jericho. But on the whole, they were a far more spiritual people than had been their forefathers, who came out of Egypt. In one area they did not obey God fully, as they failed to destroy all the pagan people of their land of promise. And so in the passing of the first generation, which had entered the promised land, the next generation began to slip further away from God in their commitment to Him. This led to the period of the judges, as God allowed their enemy nations, whom they had not wiped out, to conquer them, and then they cried out to God once again, in order to get His help in their deliverance from these enemies. Then for or a number of years, this was their pattern. They would sin, and then God would allow their enemies to conquer them, followed by a time of repentance, which attitude was soon lost, and then they were conquered again by their enemies, until they repented once again. And so the cycle continued for years. Such people can hardly be called the faithful people of God.

Finally, against God's wishes, they longed for a king, like the other nations around them, something God did not want to give them. But when they persisted, God gave them a king---a failure of a king---Saul, who was not a godly man. God then gave them a godly king in David, but that does not mean the people were a godly people, for they were not, and even David had his problems with this stubborn and stiff-necked people. Then came Solomon, a man chosen by God and gifted by God, but who eventually became a total failure, as he led the people to disobey God, as he himself took wives from the heathen nations and allowed them to build their false places of worship in the promised land. And with a king like this, the people followed in his footsteps into idolatry, though God always seemed to have a remnant---a small one at times---but there was a remnant. But the majority of God's people followed the patterns of their false leaders.

The kingdom split in 933 BC under Solomon's son, Rehoboam, into the Southern Kingdom and the Northern Kingdom, ruled by Jereboam. The Northern Kingdom had only wicked kings and by far the majority of these people were wicked as well, till the Northern Kingdom fell in 721 BC to the war-machine of Assyria. The Southern Kingdom had a mixture of good kings and bad kings, and so this kingdom as well, drifted further and further away from God. And as they did, God sent prophets to them, who they rejected also. Such a prophet was Jeremiah, who spoke God's word to God's people for the 40 years prior to the fall of Jerusalem in 586 BC. Jeremiah was hated by the people, hated by the priests, hated by the many false prophets and hated by many of the kings---though not all of them. This nation was hardly a godly nation, either.

Then, because of the Southern Kingdom's disobedience to God, many died when Jerusalem fell, while others were carried captive to the land of Babylon to spend 70 years in captivity---all because of their sin against God. They returned to their promised land with great excitement, but if we read the post-exile prophets, we find that the people soon drifted from God again, so much that it was difficult to complete the rebuilding of the temple and the walls of Jerusalem, a work they finally completed. But with the completion of the rebuilding of Jerusalem and the Temple, their hearts were soon cold towards God once more.

Thus, prior to the coming of our Lord, the next four hundred years were years of difficulty for God's people, as they were in constant battle with their enemies. Their seventy years in Babylon had cured them of their idolatrous tendencies, but their religion was eventually taken over by legalists, such as the Pharisees and Sadducees, who turned their relation to God from the warmth of true devotion to legalism and arrogant claims of their own self-righteousness and a salvation by their keeping of the law.

Then God sent His own Son into the world as one of them, a Jew, and their past unbelief and disobedience to God came to a climax, when they rejected their Messiah and nailed Him to a cross to die, and they did it with a hatred and blindness that has never been equaled. And as they did it, they proclaimed arrogantly in Matthew 27:25, "Let His blood be upon us and upon our children!" I urged Billy to remember this statement, as it would become very important in our study. Remember how they rejected their God over the years and then their Messiah, and then God rejected them, and His blood was upon His chosen people, the Jews, and God turned to the Gentiles, as we read in the book of Acts. Could this not be the context of Matthew 24---the fall of Jerusalem---and not the Second Coming?

Could not Matthew 24 contain warnings to the Jews of the first century AD for their rejection of His Son---their Messiah? Could it be that Matthew 24 is not speaking of the Second Coming of our Lord, but of the sad reality concerning the judgment of God upon His own people, the Jews, for their part in the death of His Son?

There is so much confusion over this chapter, that it must be admitted that several approaches have become prominent concerning its interpretation---

1. Some say that it speaks completely and totally concerning the Second Coming of Christ!

2. Others say that it speaks completely and totally of the destruction of Jerusalem in 70 AD!

3. Still others say that it speaks both of the Second Coming of Christ and the destruction of Jerusalem!

I told Billy that I had been taught as a young preacher the first view, which says that Matthew 24 speaks completely concerning the Second Coming of Christ! Thus, for a number of years, I had never heard any other possible view of Matthew 24. But then I learned of the two other views, and I realized I had to study this passage further concerning this matter. I acknowledged that good men had held and did now hold these three different views, and that the debate at times was hot and heavy, as to which one was the Biblical view. Does Matthew 24 speak only of the Second Coming of Christ? Or does it speak only of the Fall of Jerusalem in 70 AD? Or does it speak of both events, intermingling them in the progression of the chapter?

Billy could only say, "Wow, thaaaaat's deeeeeep!"

25

Chapter 8

After further discussion, which included questions from Billy, our study time came to an end, and we went our separate ways---his by automobile and ours to the airport to our Learjet. I had thought it would be a peaceful ride home, but when we got to the Learjet, we had two pilots that we did not recognize. Mrs. Cardieux had told us not to fly with anyone but our designated pilots, unless she had contacted us and given us the name of other pilots. When we asked these pilots their names and who had sent them, they said Mrs. Cardieux had sent them. But when we called her on the phone, she had never heard of them, and then when we came back to the plane, they were gone. With a little investigating, we found our pilots knocked out and bound and gagged and stashed in a compartment on our plane. I couldn't help but wonder what would have been our fate, had we gotten on that plane with the now missing fake pilots. There was no doubt as to who had sent them!

I was glad that we had decided Dink would go with me on these trips to the mountains, because it appeared these uncles were serious about stopping Billy from leaving them and studying with us---so serious that they were trying to get rid of us. Before we finally took off, we asked the manager of the airport, if he had seen some different pilots near our plane, and he admitted he had seen two different pilots, but just thought that they both were there legitimately. He also said he had never seen these two pilot before.

When I called Mrs. Cardieux, she told me again never to get on the plane without our appointed pilots, unless she had called and given me the name of other pilots. No sooner had I gotten off the phone with Mrs. Cardieux, than Billy called me, and when I described the false pilots to him, he knew who one false pilot was---another uncle who had a few pilot lessons and a license---but he wasn't a greatly experienced pilot, for he had only flown a plane a few times, that he knew of. Plus, he was a shady kind of character, who had been in and out of jail several times---something of a drifter, who couldn't be trusted!

Dink couldn't stop praising the Lord for His being with us---no telling what the fake pilots might have had planned for us. Dink adamantly declared that he was going with me to all of my meetings with Billy. Then when I finally got home, my phone rang again, and a strange voice (but also a southern hillbilly kind of a voice) told me that there were other ways to accomplish what they had tried to do tonight. There was something eerie about his speech and laughter, as he told me these things. Then I alerted him that we knew who he was, and he might be the one who needed to worry, if he tried anything else like he had tried earlier today. His attitude was smirky, as he asked me if I was going to contact the police about this matter? He assured me the police would only tell me that they needed more information and evidence than that. And he further assured me that he had several alibis for this morning. And then with a giant burst of sinister laughter and glee, he hung up.

I wondered how many more of the mountain boys Billy's uncles would enlist to help them get rid of us, so they could get Billy back under their control? But is there not some way we could get the police to help us in corralling them? I smiled at that thought. It would probably turn out that some of their kinfolk would be the sheriff or police chief of that community, and we wouldn't stand a chance of getting any help! I decided to call Mrs. Cardieux to ask her about the matter, and she confirmed my suspicions---the good-old-boy-police officers would take care of their own, if it was their neighbors or kin versus us uppity-up city boys!

Chapter 9

There were no problems the next Saturday, getting from Seminary City, where I lived, to the mountain area, where I was working with Billy Hill, though I was a bit concerned about the travel, both in the Learjet and the car ride to Mrs. Cardieux's home. And after having dealt with the remote context of our passage, which was a review of the entire history of the Jews in the Old Testament, which showed their blatant failure before God in every age, we were now ready to deal with the nearer context of Matthew 24, which was the context of the gospel of Matthew. In doing so, I asked them to <u>please notice the slow but certain reality, not only of the Jews' rejection of Christ, but also of Christ's turning away from the Jews</u>. We will deal mostly with the passages which pertain to this subject.

I informed them also that this section will be a little longer than most of our studies, but it is necessary that we take it as a whole for the clarity of the context and its continuity.

Chapter 1---The Genealogy of Our Lord Jesus!

Jesus had a Jewish genealogy, and He was virgin-born, as He was begotten by a Jewish girl named Mary, before she and her husband, Joseph came together in the marriage relationship. Jesus was born as the king of the Jews---to be their Messiah sent from God on their benefit and behalf. Thus, Jesus was a Jew---their Messiah.

Chapter 2---The Negative Attitude of the Jews towards Jesus Christ Begins to Show!

Herod was himself a Jew, and he wanted Jesus dead---and he even tricked the wise men, who had come miles and miles to see the baby Jesus. The wise men were Gentiles, and ironically, they came seeking the Messiah, so they could worship Him, while Herod, who is something of a picture of the Jews of Christ's day, sought to find Christ so he could kill Him. What a contrast! Is this not a summary of the Jews of Christ's day, as they had no eyes to see or understand who Christ was, while some Gentiles did? But the Jewish nation knew it not, that is, that their Messiah had been born, while Herod, the one who does know of His birth, has sought to kill Him.

Chapter 3---The Ministry of John the Baptist!

John bore witness of Christ and told the people---
    that Christ was to be preferred before Him!
    that truth and grace comes by Jesus Christ!
    that Christ is the only-begotten Son of God!
    that Christ has seen the Father!
    that Christ takes away the sin of the world!

Chapter 4---The Victory of Jesus Christ over Satan!

Though Satan tempts Christ in three ways, Satan loses the battle to get Christ to act independently of His Father. Christ is victorious and refuses to act upon Satan's false promises. It is then that the powerful ministry of Christ begins in Galilee, as Christ calls His first disciples, and they follow Him, though they do not know all that will be involved in following the Lord. Christ goes through all Galilee preaching the gospel and healing all kinds of sicknesses and diseases. His fame goes throughout all Syria and great multitudes followed Him from Galilee and Decapolis and Jerusalem and Judea and even from beyond the Jordan. To many it may have appeared that Christ had come to set up His kingdom now, but they were wrong in that idea.

Chapters 5-7---The Sermon on the Mount!

Here is the Sermon on the Mount, which takes place because of the multitudes of people who were following our Lord. Thus, He opened His mouth and taught them, and when He was finished, the people were astonished at His doctrine, as He taught as one having authority and not as the scribes and Pharisees, who always wanted to show their brilliance by uncertain debate.

Chapter 8---Evidence Christ Is Turning to the Gentiles!

Here is the healing of a Gentile---a Roman centurion's servant, plus others who were Jews. But this shows that Christ is turning from the Jewish race to the Gentile race. Take note of the centurion's words, when he spoke of his unworthiness to have Christ under his roof. And then Christ said to him *"Verily, I say unto you, I have not found so great faith, no not in Israel. And I say to you that many* (Gentiles) *shall come from the east and west, and shall sit down with Abraham and Isaac and Jacob in the kingdom of heaven. But the sons of the kingdom* (the Jews) *shall be cast out into outer darkness, where there shall be weeping and gnashing of teeth!"* Does this not show clearly a turning to the Gentiles and a turning from the Jews, and the reality of the sorrow that will follow for the Jews?

Chapter 9---Miracles and Preaching Everywhere!

This chapter shows Christ's gracious ministry in Galilee, which includes the call of Matthew and a series of miracles, which are further proof of Christ's claims. He went about all the cities and villages, preaching in their synagogues the kingdom of heaven and healing every kind of sickness and disease. It is here also that Jesus told His disciples that the harvest is plenteous, but the laborers are few.

Chapter 10---Christ Calls His Twelve Apostles!

This is the point of Christ's ministry where He calls the twelve apostles and gives them some general instructions for their ministry, and He further warns them of how they will be treated---rejection and persecution by the Jews--- and what they are to do in the hours to come. Thus, though He is in the process of turning to the Gentiles, He does call from the Jews men who will serve as His apostles!

Chapter 11---More Evidence Christ Is Rejecting the Jews!

John the Baptist in prison wonders if Christ is the Messiah. And Jesus takes another aim at the Jewish race, as He states clearly that the Jewish race is a fickle and inconsistent race. They are like children---nothing pleases them. They were not pleased with John the Baptist. They have called Jesus a glutton and a winebiber and a friend of tax-collectors and sinners. Thus, Christ further denounces this age and race of the Jewish people as a whole, and Christ pronounces "woes" on certain of their cities for not believing in Him--- Chorizin, Bethsaida, and Capernaum. Plus, He tells them that if His mighty works had been done in Sodom, which had been done in their cities, Sodom would have remained to this day. So it is clear again that the Jewish people, as a whole, are rejecting Him, and He is in the process of rejecting them.

Chapter 12---The Final Rejection of the Jews and the Acceptance of the Gentiles!

As Christ confronts the Scribes and Pharisees with the fact that He is Lord of the Sabbath, the Pharisees continue to confront Him, even while He is in the synagogue. Thus, it is clear that the Pharisees are becoming more and more confrontational and more and more are rejecting Him. The Pharisees now form a council against Christ to try to figure out how they could destroy Him---even kill Him---if necessary. Jesus withdraws from the Pharisees and gives further proof of His ministry by quoting Isaiah and then working another miracle. At this hour some of the Pharisees committed the unpardonable sin by blaspheming the Holy Spirit, which not only was a very serious action, but a clear sign to us of the reality of the Jewish rejection of our Lord. The Pharisees then demanded a sign, and He gives them two signs---His coming resurrection from the dead and the reality that a greater than Solomon was in their midst, and they did not know it. Jesus then calls them a wicked generation because of their unbelief! Could one speak any stronger against a generation of people than that? <u>Then, shockingly, He states that from now on all His previous relationships with the Jews, including family and nation, are no longer His, because He has been rejected by His own people, the nation of Israel.</u> <u>And now the Gentiles are His brethren</u>. Does this not clearly say that the Jews are no longer His people? They have rejected Him, and He is now turning away from the Jews, because of their unbelief, to another people, the Gentiles.

Chapter 13---Further Proof Of Christ's Rejection by the Jews!

Christ now tells His disciples that it is given to them to know the mysteries of the kingdom, but not to the others (the unbelieving Jews), because of their unbelief. And so

32

He gives a series of parables, which tells them some truths about the kingdom of heaven. Many were asking Him questions about His family and mighty works, trying to figure out who He was. Jesus told them in return that a prophet is not without honor except in his own country and in his own household. Which is to say, that though they acknowledge His great wisdom and power, they still are questioning His person, which will continue till His death and beyond for many! Another evidence of His rejection by the Jews.

Chapter 14---A Greater Rejection by the Jews!

By this time there should have been no doubt in the minds of the Jews about Who Christ was, but the Jewish mind for the most part was still closed to the acceptance of Jesus as their Messiah. Now even further proof of His person brings a greater rejection from the Jews. Herod begins to fear what he had done in beheading John the Baptist, but there seems to be no repentance! Jesus was moved with compassion, when He saw a large multitude of people who had found Him once again. It is at this point that He fed the 5000, clearly a miracle, and then He walked on water to the surprise of His disciples, and then He healed many in Gennesaret. His person and power is evident, but the multitudes are following Him for the benefit He brings to them, as they do not know really who He is.

Chapter 15---Rejection by the Pharisees and Acceptance by a Gentile Woman Whose Child Is Healed!

Christ's ministry brings Him into another confrontation with the Pharisees from Jerusalem, whose ire and hatred of Christ is growing. Christ tells them boldly that their traditions transgress the very commandments of God. He then exposes their true hearts of unbelief. In the midst of the Pharisees rejection of Christ, He saves a Gentile woman and also heals her child---another contrast between the Gentiles believing on Him, while His own people reject Him. Going back to the Sea of Galilee, He goes up into a mountain and a great multitude comes to Him again, as many are still seeking Him, while their leaders and many others of the common people, are rejecting Him. But the question is, do the common people understand who He is?

Chapter 16---Blindness to the Jews---Light to Apostles!

The Pharisees once again ask for a sign from heaven, but Jesus does not give them a sign---only the sign of Jonah, which they do not understand. Jesus and His disciples then go to the other side of the sea, and when the disciples remembered that they had forgotten bread, Christ then warned them of the leaven of the Pharisees, that is their false doctrine. This chapter shows that the spiritual sight of His disciples is becoming stronger, as they follow their Lord and listen to Him, but they still have much to learn. Then comes Peter's confession as he states concerning Jesus, *"Thou art the Christ, the Son of the living God."* Jesus then tells Peter that flesh and blood has not revealed this to him. Note here that if such thinking was just dawning on His apostles, what about the masses? Jesus then said that He would build His church on this rock--- which is Peter's statement that Christ is the Messiah. Christ tells them He will give them power for their ministries. Then He charges His apostles not to tell anyone that He is the Messiah, which is followed by His statement to His apostles of His coming death and resurrection, something Peter found hard to believe, and he even rebuked Christ for

34

saying such a thing. This shows us that no one knew up to this point that Christ was going to die, let alone be crucified. They were undoubtedly looking for an earthly Messiah and kingdom---remember that! Christ rebuked Peter, telling him to get behind Him, for Peter is speaking the things of men and not the things of God. Christ then began to tell His disciples something of the true cost of discipleship, but do they really understand that either?

Chapter 17---Further Evidence the Apostles Were Looking for an Earthly Kingdom!

This chapter brings to us more of the lessons Christ gave to His apostles, as He took Peter and James and John up on a high mountain apart. There He was transfigured before them, and Christ's face shone like the sun, and His clothing was as white as the light. Then Moses and Elijah appeared and talked with Christ! God then spoke, telling them that Christ was His beloved Son---in Whom God was well pleased. When the apostles had come down to the masses, they were unable to cast out a demon, and Christ told them it was because of their unbelief. Could it be that Christ's further revelation of Himself to them had caused them to wonder even further who Christ was and what was to come in the future and how it would effect them and their lives? And could their unbelief also be because of their confusion and questions as to who Christ was, since He had just recently told them of His coming death? Then Jesus again finally and bluntly tells His apostles of His coming betrayal and death, but also that He would rise again---something, which made the apostles quite sad. This certainly seems to indicate that this is the first time such a truth had really sunk into their minds in its reality---though He had told them before. But now it seems to sink in---He is going to die? And it surely shows they had been looking for an earthly kingdom, which they should now realize is not coming. But old ideas are difficult to lose.

Chapter 18---The Shallowness of the Apostles Thinking!

This chapter shows that the previous statements of Jesus concerning His death have not penetrated His apostles' minds, perhaps simply because they could not grasp such a thought and didn't want to believe such a thing. This shallowness is seen, as Christ finds them debating who will be the greatest in the kingdom of heaven. Christ gives them some basic principles, which should contradict their desires for greatness. They must become as little children to enter the kingdom of heaven. Greatness should not be their goal, but the humility of a child should be their demeanor. Plus, they must realize the seriousness of sin---particularly the sin of offending others. He tells them they must do everything and anything they can to be rid of sin. If the hand or foot causes one to sin---cut it off---for it is better to enter into life maimed than to be in hell with all ones bodily extremities. Obviously, Christ speaks here again in symbolic language and not with literal speech, but even at that, His speech is quite impacting and no doubt raised some questions.

**Chapter 19---Further Lessons
for the Disciples and the Pharisees!**

We see again the scheming hearts of the Pharisees, as they come to try to trap Jesus, concerning the lawfulness of a man putting away his wife for every cause, which some of their teachers claimed a man could do. Christ deals with that question by telling them marriage includes a one-flesh relationship, which cannot be broken except by adultery. Later in this chapter the apostles deny children to come to Jesus for prayer, but Jesus tells them clearly to allow the little children to come to Him---for of such is the kingdom of heaven. Another man asks what he must do to gain eternal life, and then he says he has kept the commandments from his youth. Christ tells him to go and sell all he has and give it to the poor, and then come and follow Him. When the man heard this, he went away sorrowfully. Christ knew this man was depending upon his works, and that Christ's words were a trial of the young man's claim of having done all which the law required. Christ's disciples wondered then who could enter the kingdom of heaven? Christ assures them they are to forsake all to follow Him, but He is not teaching a works salvation, but that godly works will follow a true salvation.

Chapter 20---A Contrast between Jews and Gentiles!

The parable of the householder and laborers show us again the contrast between the Gentiles and the Jews. The laborers came to work for the householder at various hours---some earlier and some later---but their wages were the same. This parable pictures the Jews, who were the early followers of God, while the Gentiles were the "Johnny come latelies" in the matter of salvation, and they are the ones the Jews despised. The Jews are convinced that they are God's chosen people. But Christ is making it clear that the Gentiles, those who come to God later in history, will be part of the body of Christ also, while many of the Jews will miss out on the reality of true salvation. Later in this chapter, we find Christ and his disciples moving towards Jerusalem. Christ reveals to them that when they get to Jerusalem, He will be betrayed and given up to the chief priests and scribes, and He will be condemned to die and He will be mocked and scourged and crucified. But He will rise the third day. But then comes something way out of order, in light of what has just been said, when the mother of James and John asks that her sons might sit, one on His right hand and the other on His left hand in His kingdom, <u>Does this not tell us of the possibility that many of them, including His apostles, did not take seriously His words of His coming death</u>? James and John even assure Him they are able to drink of the cup He drinks of and be baptized with His baptism, but do they realize Christ is speaking of His death here? Christ says that will be true---they will drink of His cup and be baptized with His baptism---even though they may not understand at this hour what this all means---death. Then He tells them that to give them a position on His right or left hand in the kingdom, is not His to give. Thus, it seems clear that these apostles and the other Jews were still looking for an earthly kingdom, rather than a spiritual and heavenly one,

Chapter 21---The Jewish Race---A Barren Fig Tree!

This important chapter shows us Christ's triumphal entry on into the city of Jerusalem as the King of Glory. He then cleanses the temple, stating His house is to be called a house of prayer, but they have made it a den of thieves. Then He uses a barren fig tree to picture the Jewish nation, as they are spiritually barren and will be after His death. Following this, the chief priests and elders challenge Christ's authority, and Christ wins that battle. This is followed by the parable of the two sons--one said he would go and work in his father's vineyard, but he did not go, while the other said he would not go and work, but later he did. This again surely pictures the Jews and the Gentiles.

The Jews claimed to be God's people, but they were anything but the people of God at this hour. The Gentiles said they would not go work in God's vineyard, and later they did. This caused Jesus to tell the priests and elders of the Jews that the tax collectors and the harlots would enter into His kingdom before they would. This is a clear rejection of His own people, the Jews. Finally, in this section we have the parable of the householder, who owned a piece of property, and he engaged certain men to care for his property. When the householder sent his servants to the men overseeing his property, they killed the servants. They did this several times. Finally the householder sent his own son, saying surely they will honor my son. But they killed his son also. When Jesus asked the Jewish leaders what the householder should do with these wicked men, who had killed his servants and son, they replied, "The owner of the vineyard will put these wicked men to a horrible death!" Clearly, these Jews did not see this as a picture of them and their responsibility before God. They too had rejected God and His will for them, and they took over God's work for themselves, and they killed the prophets, who God had sent to them, and when God finally sent His own Son, they killed Him too. Is this not a hint of what what God the Father will do to these wicked Pharisees and Jews and their supposedly holy city, Jerusalem, as they have killed God's Son, Jesus Christ?

Chapter 22---Christ Clashes with the Pharisees and Sadducees and They Cannot Answer Him!

This chapter once again speaks to the Jews, as it contains several clashes between Christ and the Pharisees and Saducees, and Christ always wins in the confrontations. First, there is the parable of the wedding feast given by a king. Those invited do not attend, so others are invited and they come. Obviously this pictures the Jews, who are invited to come to Christ and they refuse, and the Gentiles are those not first invited, and when invited they do come to the wedding feast.

Then the Pharisees and the Sadducees separately try to corner Christ with the Pharisees asking Him about paying tribute to Caesar, and Christ answers, "Render to Caesar what is Caesar's and render to God what is God's!" The Sadducees quiz Christ with a fictitious story, as they denied any kind of a resurrection, and He answers there is no marriage in heaven.

The Pharisees then again try to trip Christ concerning which is the greatest of the commandments of the law of God. Christ then gives a brief summary of all the laws when He says, *Thou shalt love the Lord thy God with all thy heart! Thou shalt love the lord thy God with all thy soul! Thou shalt love the Lord thy God with all thy mind! Thou shalt love thy neighbor as thyself!* Then Christ asked the Pharisees, *What do you think of the Messiah? Whose Son is He?* They answered Him in return, *The Messiah is the Son of David!* Jesus then asked them why then did David call the Messiah, Lord, and He then quoted Psalm 110:1, *The Lord said to my Lord, sit at my right hand till I put your enemies under your feet!* And then He asked the Pharisees, *If David calls the Messiah Lord, then how can He be David's son?* We then read, *From that day on no one dared ask him any more questions.*

Chapter 23---The Hypocrisy of the Pharisees!

This is the chapter where Christ totally chastises and recognizes for all to see and understand the reality of the blatant hypocrisy of the Pharisees. And He was speaking to the multitude and His disciples when He said these things. Christ then gives a long list of the hypocrisy of the actions of the Pharisees.

The Pharisees love authority!

They expect others to obey their laws, but they do not!

They lay heavy burdens on the backs of others!

They give others no help to bear those burdens!

They do what they do for their own glory before men!

They love the uppermost places of honor at the feasts!

They love the most important seats in the synagogues!

They love to be greeted in the market-place!

They love to have men call them "Rabbi!"

They are not to be called "Rabbi!"

They are not to call any man on earth "father!"

He that is the greatest will be their servant!

If one exalts himself---he will be humbled!

If anyone humbles himself---he will be exalted!

The Lord then pronounces on the Pharisees various woes, and He ends up calling them snakes and a generation of vipers who shall not escape the damnation of hell. They have crucified and killed the prophets and flogged them and chased them from city to city. Thus, upon these Pharisees will the righteous blood fall which has been shed on earth from the blood of Able to the blood of Zechariah. AND CHRIST TELLS THEM THAT THESE JUDGMENTS WILL FALL ON THIS GENERATION.

Our Lord is then filled with deep sorrow, as He weeps over Jerusalem and says, *O Jerusalem, Jerusalem---you who kill the prophets and stone those sent to you! How often I have longed to gather your children together, as a hen gathers her chicks under her wings---but you were not willing! Behold your house will be left unto you desolate! You will not see me again until you say, Blessed is he who comes in the name of the Lord!*

Final Comments on Our Subject!

Barnes comments on this verse as he says Christ is saying to the Jews----

> Ye shall not see me---the day of mercy for you is gone. I have offered you protection and salvation and you have rejected it. You are about to crucify me, and your temple will be destroyed, and you, as a nation, will be given up to long and dreadful suffering. You will not see me as a merciful Saviour, offering you redemption any more, until you have borne these heavy judgments. These things must come upon you, and be borne until you will be glad to hail a deliverer, and say---Blessed is He that cometh in the name of the Lord! Blessed be He that comes as the Messiah to bring deliverance!

I then asked Billy to read these chapters several times before the next week, and to understand what we mean when we say that these chapters give us the immediate context of Matthew 24. Billy's final words to me were in his southern brogue, "I see what you mean when you say context is king! Boy and is it ever!

Thus we have seen in the context of Matthew---
The final rejection of Christ by the Jews is clear!
The final rejection of the Jews by Christ is final!
The coming salvation of Gentiles is stated!
The future of Christ's ministry is unknown to them!
The apostles are struggling with all of this!
The future of their city is unknown to them!
All of this is the context of Matthew 24 as Christ
seeks to prepare them for their immediate
future---not for our future!

From the context of the failure of the Jews in the OT to the failure of the Jews in the NT, the answers concerning the subject of Matthew 24 should be very clear. Matthew 24 is in the clear context of the events of the past Old Testament history and the events unfolding in the New Testament---the final failure of the Jews and God's rejection of them in the New Testament era. Therefore, as we approach Matthew 24, we say again, we would be very wrong to approach it with the context of our day. We must put ourselves in the context of the apostles, as they struggled all through the early days of their discipleship and apostleship with the question of Who Christ was and what He had come to do. We say again that the context of Matthew's gospel is not a context of our day, and Christ's followers were not looking forward to His death and Second Coming. It was only after His death and resurrection that the future became clear to them on these things, The proof of their ignorance of His death and resurrection, though Christ had warned them concerning these things, is that when Christ died, His disciples scattered with an uncertainty of the past and what really had happened or what the future would bring them. They couldn't even begin to imagine that He would rise from the dead, and it was not till Christ's resurrection that they were given an understanding and power by the Holy Spirit to stand boldly for the truth---in light of the fact that He was alive.

Thus, we say again that they were not thinking about any Second Coming of Christ---they were trying to understand what He would do from the basis of His first coming with His claim to be their Messiah. A Second Coming was the furthest thing from their minds at this hour. They had questioned all of His statements concerning His coming death, and when He had tried to explain it all to them, when He said they would be baptized with His baptism, referring to His death, they seemed to think that

43

whatever kind of baptism it was, it was something which was easy and not any reference to persecution and death.

We must remember this reality and fact when we come to our next chapter, for so many have just jumped into the twenty-forth chapter of Matthew without any concern or understanding of what we have just seen as the context of Matthew, which we have tried to carefully cover chapter by chapter. We have seen the reality and certainty of His emphasis on His coming death and that He was speaking not the reality of a Second Coming off in the distant future of the history of the church.

I apologized for taking so long, but I told them there was no way we could study Matthew 24, which we would take up in our next study, without a clear understanding of the context of the whole of the book of Matthew. They all shook their heads, as if they understood, even Billy, as he continued to have something of a puzzled look on his face. I didn't know if it was the evidence that he had understood something for the first time, or if he was still struggling to understand the fullness of our study.

Chapter 10

I must confess that I was really tired by the time Dink and I got back to our plane for the ride home. It had been a long day and it would be a longer day by the time we got home---even if all things went well. I must admit, I was in no mood for any extra-curricular activities that the uncles of Billy or anyone else might dig up to frustrate us this night, either before we got on our plane or while we were on the plane or when we got off the plane in our own home town. As we flew through the air, I sat dozing and asleep and hardly noticed anything, till I heard the engines beginning to sputter, as if they were out of fuel.

Dink noticed this before I did, and he had gone up to the cockpit to see what was taking place. When he came back, he acknowledged that it was one of the engines and that the pilots were going to try to hobble in on one engine. Somehow I didn't exactly like those words--- "hobble in" and "on one engine!" But then all of a sudden the sputtering stopped and the plane ran as smooth as silk the rest of the way home. Not knowing anything about jet engines, nor did Dink, we had no way to try to understand what could have gone wrong. And when we landed the pilots had no idea either.

I must say I was glad to be back on the ground, even though it was getting late, but it troubled me that something had come up like this again. How many more times would we face something like this. I asked one of the pilots if he was going to get someone to take a good look at the engine before he headed back home? He said he would do that tomorrow, since things were shut down for the night at the airport.

As Dink and I walked to our car, I wondered who might be out there in the dark tonight to hit us again, if that is what had taken place on the airplane? One could almost become paranoid, if he was not convinced that God was a sovereign God, who was in control of all things. But sure enough, when we got to the car, there was a piece of paper on the windshield of the automobile, which read,

Some men fly and some men drive,
But we will get you dead or alive!

There was no signature, but I looked at Dink and he looked at me, and we both began to shake our heads. I finally said softy, "Well, Dink, it makes no difference whether we work with city folks or country folks or mountain folks---we're always at the wrong end of someone's complaints against us!"

I said it with a smile, but Dink had no smile when he said, "Country folks or city folks---dey all has der ignoramuses, as well as der good folks! But I knows a couple of dose country ignoramuses, who if dey ain't careful is gonna get der grits beat outta dem!"

About that time he found something else on the ground next to the front door of the car---it was somebody's card that had been dropped, accidentally, so it seemed. When we got in the car, the dome light allowed us to read the name on it, and sure enough, it bore the name of one of Billy's uncles. Surely, he had not left the card on the ground on purpose---how dumb can one be. Either way, we had no certain proof of anything that would stand up in court, as to who left the little note on the windshield or why someone might leave one of the uncle's cards on the ground.

But we knew someone had been around our car, and it seems they were trying to scare us off. And it seemed again that we needed to take their scare seriously. But was there some way we could set a trap for them and catch them red-handed doing their dirty work?

For now, we decided we would sleep on it.

Chapter 11

Dink and I wondered all that next week if our plane was coming for us on Saturday. And finally, Mrs. Cardieux called and assured us that they had found nothing wrong with the plane, but just for safety's sake, they had placed a guard on the plane twenty-four hours a day since then. Thus, with some trepidation we were back on the plane early the next Saturday morning, headed for the mountain country. And to our great delight, all went well on the flight---not a whimper from anyone or anything---even from our engines. Billy was right on time, and soon we were into our study of Matthew 24.

After our normal greetings, I turned to Billy and asked him if he had made something of a summary of the book of Matthew concerning God and His dealing with the Jews. Eagerly, he pulled out several pieces of paper, and he distributed to each of us a copy of what he had done in way of summation of the book of Matthew, Chapters 1-23. And then he led us through it explaining it all in great depth and in a very impressive manner. Following is a summary of his work.

A SMALLER SUMMARY OF
the Gospel of Matthew 1-23
with Reference to the Jewish and Gentile Races
and Their Relationship with God!

Chapter 2---There is the clear contrast of the Gentiles and the Jews in the reality of Herod, a Jew, who was seeking to kill Christ as a baby, and the Gentile wise men who came from afar to worship Christ as the Messiah at His birth!

Chapter 3---There again is the contrast of the message of John the Baptist, the prophet of God, who pointed out Christ to the Jews of His day, but the Pharisees and

Sadducees from Jerusalem, were Jews of spiritual darkness, keeping others from coming to Christ also.

Chapter 8---In this chapter we see a Gentile Roman centurion, who asked Christ to heal his servant, and Christ did just that. The centurion then spoke with such humility and grace, as he said he was unworthy to have Christ under his roof. Christ then commended him as a man who had a greater faith than anyone He had seen in Israel (which includes the Jews), and Christ added that He would sit down in His kingdom with all kinds of races of men, but the sons of the kingdom (the Jews) will be cast out into outer darkness, where there shall be weeping and gnashing of teeth.

Chapter 11---Christ states that the Jewish race is a fickle and inconsistent race. They are like children in that nothing pleases them. They have called Jesus a glutton and a winebibber and a friend of tax-collectors and sinners. Christ responds by pronouncing certain "woes" on certain of their Jewish cities--Chorizin, Bethsaida and Capernaum. He then tells them that if the mighty works had been done in Sodom, which have been done during His ministry in present-day Jewish cities, Sodom would have remained till this day.

Chapter 12---As the Jews become more and more confrontational against Christ, it then becomes known that the Pharisees at this point form a council against Him to try to figure out how they could destroy Him---even kill Him. When they blaspheme the Holy Spirit, Christ calls them a wicked generation because of their unbelief. He then states that from now on all His previous relationships with the Jews, including family and nation, are no longer His---

48

for those relationships are gone, because He has been rejected by His own people, the nation of Israel. And now the Gentiles are His brethren. He has clearly and undeniably turned away from the Jews to the Gentiles.

Chapter 13---This chapter fortresses the above statement that Christ is turning away from the unbelieving Jews, and He is now giving to the Gentiles the ability to know the mysteries of the kingdom, but not to the unbelieving Jews. Then He gives them several parables, and He tells them that a prophet is not honored in his own country, not even by his own household.

Chapter 15---Christ saves a Gentile woman in the midst of His rejection by the Pharisees, and He also heals this woman's child---what a contrast.

Chapter 16---This chapter shows the great unbelief of the Pharisees, as they ask for a sign from heaven. But Jesus does not give them a sign---but they will be given only the sign of Jonah---which statement they do not understand. It is a statement of His coming resurrection from the dead. This is also the chapter of Peter's statement that, *Thou art the Christ (the Messiah), the Son of the living God!* But the great majority of the Jews, especially the Pharisees, would not accept this statement. Christ then charges His apostles not to tell any one that He is the Messiah.

Chapter 17---This is the chapter of Christ's transfiguration before three of His apostles in the mountain. Moses and even Elijah appeared and talked with Christ. God even spoke to the three apostles who were present, telling them that Christ was His beloved Son in whom He was well-pleased. Later after coming down from the mountain,

Christ tells them He is going to be betrayed and He will die, and even though He has told them of His death before, now it seems to sink in much deeper. They surely understand that He is going to be killed by the Jews.

Chapter 19---This chapter shows us further of the scheming hearts of the Pharisees, as they come to try to trap Jesus in His words.

Chapter 20---Christ in the parable of the householders and laborers, makes it clear again that the Gentiles will be part of the body of Christ, while Jews will miss out on the reality of true salvation. Christ also tells them in this chapter, much to their shock and amazement, that when they go to Jerusalem, He will be betrayed and given up to the chief priests and scribes, and He will be condemned to death. In the process He will be mocked and scourged and crucified, but He will rise the third day. Thus, His death is coming by means of the Jews.

Chapter 21---In this chapter Christ shows them a barren fig tree, which surely represents the nation of the Jews, as they are spiritually barren and will be even after His death. Christ later in this chapter speaks the parable of the two sons---one who said he would go and work in his father's vineyard and he did not do it. The other said he would not go and work in His father's vineyard, but later he did so. This again is surely a picture of the Jews and the Gentiles. The Jews claimed to be God's people, but then they became anything but the people of God in the passing of their history, as they would not work in His vineyard. The Gentiles were not the people of God, and they would not work in God's vineyard to begin with, but later they did. Jesus then tells the priests and elders of the Jews that the tax collectors and the harlots would enter into His kingdom before they would.

Chapter 21 further---This chapter has the parable of a householder, who left his property in the hands of men. But when the householder sent his servants to inspect matters, the servants were killed by these men, who were supposed to be caring for the householder's property. Finally the householder sent his own son, thinking they would honor his own son. But instead they killed him also. Obviously, this pictures the Pharisees and Jews who had killed the prophets, and now they are going to kill God's Son.

Chapter 22---This is another parable, which pictures the Jews of Christ's day. A king (who pictures God) has a wedding feast for his son (who pictures Christ), and many are are invited to come (the Jews of that day and past history), but they never came to the wedding feast. The king then sends out his servants into the highways and hedges and gathers all the people they could find, and the wedding hall was filled with guests. This parable surely speaks of the failure of God's OT people and the grace of God now being received by the Gentiles.

Chapter 23---This chapter speaks of Christ totally chastising the Pharisees for all to see and to understand the reality of the blatant hypocrisy of the Pharisees. And He was speaking to the multitude and His disciples, when He said these things, which shows that this scathing rebuke goes out for all the Jews to hear. After this rebuke, He then pronounces upon the Pharisees various woes. How shall they ever escape the damnation of hell? They have crucified and killed the prophets! Upon them will fall the righteous blood of the men they killed, who were faithful to God unto death! Christ then says that <u>all of the coming judgments will fall upon this generation</u> (not ours but the generation of these He was upbraiding now at this very hour and moment)! Then our Lord with deep sorrow weeps over Jerusalem as He says, *O Jerusalem, Jerusalem---you who kill the prophets and stoned those sent to you. How often I have longed to gather your children together, as a hen gathers her chicks under her wings--but you were not willing. Behold your house will be left unto you desolate. You will not see me again until you say, Blessed is he who comes in the name of the Lord.*

Final Summary and Conclusions!

From the context of the failure of the Jews in both the OT and the NT (including Matthew) the meaning of Matthew 24 should be very clear. Matthew 24 is the final prediction of the fall of Jerusalem, because of the Jews rejection of Christ and God's rejection of the Jews. This confirms that we would be wrong to approach Matthew 24 with the context of our day.

I had to admit that Billy's summary was a very good summary of my summary. Clearly, he had understood what I had said, that is, that we must consider the context of Matthew 1-23 as we come to study Matthew 24. This surely points out the problem with many or our day, who would come to Matthew 24 without having considered the context of their day, but they only go fishing for something that can be related to our own day. That approach may sound good to many, but it fails to recognize the context of the whole Bible and the previous chapters of the book of Matthew in relationship to the entire Jewish history.

Chapter 12

The trip home was uneventful, and things were quiet in our city for the next week, even concerning Billy's uncles ---not a word from anyone about anything. But soon it was time to get on back to the mountain area for another study with Billy. When we landed, we were surprised when Mrs. Cardieux was there to meet us with some rather shocking news. Billy had gotten engaged to the daughter of a lost man this past week, and there was some question about her salvation also, though she was a church member.

As we drove to her house, which was our place of study, Mrs. Cardieux said Billy's engagement was a surprise to her. She didn't even know he had a girl friend. He had said nothing to her about the matter, and therefore she was convinced that his uncles, unbeknown to Billy, had put her up to this little marriage trap, so they all could get back in on Billy's money. We decided that we had better wait till our study was over, before we asked Billy about this surprise engagement. So, when he arrived, we turned to look at Matthew once again.

The Setting of Matthew 24!

The setting of Matthew 24 begins with the hour when Christ is leaving the temple area with His disciples for the last time, and He knew He was facing very soon a cruel death on the cross. But His disciples at this hour were not as knowledgeable of the future as our Lord was, for He knew His days on earth were numbered. He knew again that He would soon be arrested and tried and sentenced to die. He knew He would be nailed to a cross by His own people, the Jews. He knew also that within 40 years after His death, this temple area, which Christ and His disciples were now leaving, as recorded in the early verses of Chapter 24, would soon lie in ruins, and Jerusalem itself would be in shambles along with the death of many of the Jewish people and their leaders. Christ knew all of these future events were coming. His disciples knew none of these events were awaiting them in the future.

Instead, they were marveling, as they were leaving the temple area---marveling over its beauty and wonder. And then to their amazement, Christ spoke some frightening and unexpected words in these early verses of chapter 24. Verse 1 says that as they were leaving the temple grounds, His disciples called His attention to the magnificence of these temple buildings. There were the stones of enormous sizes, and the temple itself seemed to them to be indestructible, Then Christ's apostles became intent on pointing to the outward splendor of the temple, and they may even have been doing this to show that surely it could never be destroyed. Thus, it seems clear that they had no understanding of the future of the city of Jerusalem or of their temple, that is, that Jerusalem and the temple would be lying in ruins by 70 AD, because of the powerful forces of the Roman Empire under Titus, and because of the unfaithfulness of these Jews to their Messiah.

In verse 2 Jesus replied, pointing out to them again all these buildings, but His words were not to marvel over these structures. His speaking to them was to tell them the truth, that not one of these stones here would be left on top of the other. Every stone would be thrown down in the future in a coming day of judgment. This absolutely must have been a shock to His apostles, for no event could have seemed more improbable to them than this---the temple being destroyed and not one stone left on top of the other. How could this be? The temple was vast and rich and splendid and the pride of the Jewish nation, and they were at this hour at peace. So the confidence of the Jews, including the apostles, concerning their Temple standing for years to come, was very strong at this hour, and surely the waves of past persecution and destruction from other nations was over, and peace seemed certain in their minds concerning their holy city of Jerusalem.

But to their surprise Jerusalem did fall to the Romans, commanded by Titus in 70 AD, and the account of the siege and destruction of Jerusalem has been left to us by Josephus, a well respected witness with a clear veracity and faithfulness to the truth. In fact Josephus was a Jewish priest, and during the war with Rome he fell into the hands of the Romans, and he remained a captive during the siege and destruction of Jerusalem. Thus, he gives in his writings a running commentary of what took place at this horrible hour of Jerusalem's destruction in 70 AD, as Jesus predicted in Matthew 24. Josephus wrote of that hour---

> Caesar gave orders that they should not demolish the entire city and temple, but leave as many of the towers standing, as they were of the greatest eminency...and so much of the wall as enclosed the city on the west side. This wall was spared in order to afford a camp for such as were to lie in garrison; as were the towers also spared in order to demonstrate to posterity what kind of a city it was, and how well fortified, which the Roman valor had subdued; but for all the rest of the wall, it was so thoroughly laid even with the ground by those that dug it up to the foundation, that there was left nothing to make those that came thither believe it had ever been inhabited. (Josephus, v., p. 473)

So it would be true that this statement by our Lord concerning the coming destruction of the temple would not only have been a shock to all Jews, had they heard it, but it can be said with assurance, that His disciples would not at first have believed it. Jerusalem destroyed? The Temple destroyed? These large and magnificent stones would be strewn all over the place with not one left on top of the other? Did we understand Christ correctly? Yes, that is what He said, and this is the setting of the 24th chapter of Matthew.

A Puzzling Set of Questions
from Christ's Disciples at This Crucial Hour!

It is in verse 3 that the disciples of our Lord later asked the questions in response to Christ's shocking statements. They came to Him, when He had reached the Mount of Olives, and as they found Him sitting there alone and in privacy, they asked their questions. We also must remember the context, as they have just been told of the coming destruction of Jerusalem, and their questions must be seen in the reality of that shock and context and that context alone---again, not a context of our day!.

Question 1---When will these things be or take place?

This is surely an understandable question for them to ask of our Lord---when such tragic events will take place---that is, when will the temple and city of Jerusalem be destroyed and in such a vivid and catastrophic manner?

Question 2---What will be the sign of your coming?

This cannot be speaking of Christ's second coming, because up to this hour they had been and still were looking for an earthly kingdom. Remember the question of who would sit on His right hand and left hand in His kingdom? Remember the revulsion and

56

unbelief when Christ mentioned His death? They had been reared and had embraced even further, when they became a follower of the Lord, that He had come to set up a kingdom on earth, and they had no understanding of His death. So they believed, one way or another, that they soon would be reigning with Him on earth. Their concern at this moment was when Christ would reveal Himself and His power to the world? This is part of their view of their Messiah, as they had been told and taught as they grew up. Their idea of their Jewish Messiah was that He was going to rise up and destroy the Gentiles nations around them, but also He would reveal Himself clearly to His own people, the Jews, in the process as well, as He would be a man of great power. Thus, they were looking for His soon coming manifestation of His power, as He would become a king, who would rule the earth. To think at this point that they were speaking of events thousands of years away from their age is way out of context.

Question 3---What will be the sign of the end of this age?

Some translate this as---What will be the sign of the end of this world. But the Greek word here is not kosmos---the usual word for world---but it is aionos---which means an age. So it is more proper to translate this as---"What will be the sign of the end of this age---our age?" Obviously, they thought their present age would end and Christ would lead them into a new Jewish age, where He would rule and reign and defeat the Gentile enemies of God, and the Jews would rule and reign with Him in the years to come. Was this not the old Jewish hope for the Messiah? So they believed that a catastrophic hour was coming soon, when Christ would reveal Himself to the world, and that is when they would rule with Him. They thought it would be an hour of great victory for them and their Lord, as He would also reveal Himself to all by His powerful presence. They also asked for a sign of when this momentous hour of the end of this age would come and when a new age would begin, as He would be crowned openly as the Messiah for all to see, so they thought.

I told them I knew they would find other explanations of these three questions, but from my study, this is the one that fits the context of the disciples' day and the events which the apostles thought were soon to take place concerning their Messiah, though they were wrong. And this is the reason for the apostles disappointment and scattering, when Christ was crucified. Their minds had to be re-directed from their old ideas, when Jesus rose from the dead. But that is in the future in our text---His disciples are now trying to figure out what Jesus will do next.

After a good time of discussion, we brought our study to a close. Before we left, I asked Billy how his ministry was going. and he replied kiddingly that he had so many meetings that we could have some of them, if we wanted them. I told him I had enough already to keep me busy, and then he told us what we already knew---he was getting married, and he wanted us to perform the ceremony. When I asked him her name, he said it was "Susie Belle McCoy!" Then he added, "And--she--loves---Jesus--too!" I told him we would need to talk to them both, before agreeing to marry them. But I had to admit later to Dink, that I had no intention of putting any approval on their marriage, unless she gave clear evidence of being saved.

As our plane was making its way home, and as I was dozing comfortably, some clear thoughts came to my mind, as I contemplated the girl Billy was going to marry. We did not know this girl or how well he knew her? Who was she? He was such a common and down to earth kid, who seemed to trust everybody. Could this girl be a plant by Billy's uncles, as another way to get to his money? Would this not be the ruination of Billy's ministry, if he married the wrong girl? These are the questions we would ask him, when we met with him and then with them both.

He had gone on and on, even at this hour to try to explain to us what a nice girl she was, and that she would make the perfect preacher's wife, and that she knew her Bible very well, etc. and etc. When I asked him where he had met her, he said that she came up to him one night after his preaching, and she needed a ride home. So he gave her a ride home, and they hit if off so well that he had seen her every night since, as she came to hear him preach---every night. He said she was very shy, and he hadn't even kissed her yet, and he didn't plan to do so till they were married. Talk about a fast engagement, which had the foul smell of someone seeking to get Billy's money---and the foul smell seemed to be that of his future bride.

I always try to keep my nose out of other people's business, but surely there was something we could do to stop the speed of this marriage, which was coming down the track like a runaway freight train. Mrs. Cardieux was livid and convinced the girl had been put up to this little trick by Billy's uncles---her brothers. She wanted us to stop the freight train bearing down on Billy, and she asked us to help her in this dilemma.

I must admit, I was not sure what could be done, when a simple boy like Billy had been fooled, not once but several times by his brothers and others. And could anyone prove to him now that she was not the girl for him?

Chapter 13

Soon we found it was Saturday again (how those Saturdays do roll around), and we were on our way in the Learjet again to meet with Billy. Dink and I both agreed, that having been told so bluntly concerning Billy and his girl friend and their marriage, the next question was what we could do to stop it. Perhaps the Lord would give us some idea, after our study, as we talked with Billy further.

As we began our study, we reviewed the context of our previous studies, reminding ourselves that God's chosen people, the Jews, were a failure spiritually in the unfolding of the setting of Matthew 24. We had seen the clear evidence and statements that God was turning from them, and that He would deal with them severely in judgment, even the rejection of the Old Testament people, as God would then turn to the Gentiles.

We had seen also in our study of Matthew 24, several things in the context of the first several verses, which verses showed us Jesus leaving the temple and His disciples showing Him the buildings of the temple. In this context Jesus made a very shocking statement whereby He said that the temple would be destroyed in the future and not one stone of the temple would remain on top of the other. Later His disciples came to Him as He was seated on the Mount of Olives and asked Him three questions!

1. When shall these things be---that is the destruction of the temple, etc?
2. What will be the sign of Your coming?
3. Third, what will the be sign of the end of this age?

We noted further that the context was speaking of the time of the destruction of the temple and Jerusalem in 70 AD, and Christ was not talking of His Second Coming, but of an hour of His coming in power to deal with the Jews in judgment, which would also be the hour of the end of this present Jewish age and the beginning of a new age---in their minds. We now turned to show that this chapter of Matthew 24 concerned their age and their time.

The Reality of Their Age and Time Is Clearly Shown in the Unfolding of Christ's Message for Them!

I first read to them the next verses we would be dealing with in Matthew 24, and asked them if there was any textual evidence of whom and to whom Christ was speaking in verses 4-28---the New Testament days or the future days---even our present days of His Second Coming?

verse 4
> And Jesus answered and said unto them, Take heed that no man deceive YOU!

verse 5
> For many shall come in my name, saying, I am the Christ, and they shall deceive many!

verse 6
> And YE shall hear of wars and rumors of wars!
> See that YE be not troubled!
> For all these things must come to pass,
>   but the end is not yet!

verse 7
> For nation shall rise against nation!
> And kingdom shall rise against kingdom!
> And there shall be famines and pestilences
>   and earthquakes in various places!

verse 8
> All these are the beginning of sorrows!

verse 9
> Then shall they deliver YOU up to be afflicted!
> They shall kill YOU!

And <u>YOU</u> shall be hated by all nations for my name's sake!

verse 10

And then shall many be offended and shall betray one another and shall hate one another!

verse 11

And many false prophets shall arise and deceive many!

verse 12

And because iniquity shall abound, the love of many will wax cold!

verse 13

But he that shall endure to the end, the same shall be saved!

verse 14

And this gospel shall be preached in all the world for a witness unto all nations, and then shall the end come!

verse 15

When <u>YE</u> therefore shall see the abomination of desolation, spoken of by Daniel the prophet, stand in the in the holy place (whosoever readeth, let him understand)! (the desolation of the temple at the fall of Jerusalem!)

verse 16

Let them who are IN JUDEA flee into the mountains!

verse 17

Let him who is on the housetop not come down to take anything out of his house!

verse 18

Neither let him who is in the field return back to get his clothes!

verse 19

And woe unto those who are with child, and to those who are nursing children in those days!

verse 20

But pray that your flight be not in the winter, neither
ON THE SABBATH DAY!

verse 21

For then shall be great tribulation, such as was not since
the beginning of the world to this time, no, nor ever
shall be!

verse 22

And except those days should be shortened, there
should no flesh be saved, but for the elect's sake
those days shall be shortened!

verse 23

Then, if any man shall say unto YOU, Lo, here is
Christ, or there, believe it not!

verse 24

For there shall arise false Christs and false prophets,
and they shall show great signs and wonders,
insomuch, that if it were possible, they shall
deceive the very elect!

verse 25

Behold, I have told YOU before!

verse 26

Wherefore, if they shall say unto YOU, Behold, He is
in the desert, go not forth! Behold, he is in the secret
chambers, believe it not!

verse 27

For as the lightening comes out of the east & shines to
the west, so shall the coming of the Son of man be be!

verse 28

For wherever the carcass is, there will the eagles be
gathered together!

A careful reading of these verses convinces anyone
that Christ is speaking of the days of the apostles. I would

set before us for our certain understanding the following evidence that these verses do not speak of our modern days but of the days of our Lord's apostles!

I <u>Notice first that this section of Scripture makes use of personal pronouns that clearly show this section is spoken to and about the disciples and apostles of Christ's day and not some people in the far-off future!</u>

Christ uses the pronoun of "you" and "ye" and He is clearly addressing those in His presence at this moment as He speaks these words!
It is not "they" or "them" but "you" and "ye"!
Plus the whole passage shows Christ is speaking to those of His day!
Just in case someone missed it---here it is again---note the personal pronouns and other expressions!

verse 4
Take heed that no man deceive <u>YOU</u>!
verse 6
And <u>YE</u> shall hear of wars and rumors of wars!
See that <u>YE</u> be not troubled!
verse 9
Then shall they deliver <u>YOU</u> up to be afflicted!
They shall kill <u>YOU</u>!
<u>YOU</u> shall be hated of all nations for my namesake!
verse 15
Then <u>YE</u> shall see the abomination of desolation!
verse 16
Then let <u>THEM</u> who are in Judea flee into the mountains!
verse 17
Let <u>HIM</u> who is on the housetop not come down to take anything out of his house!

verse 18
> Neither let <u>HIM</u> who is in the fields return back to take HIS clothes!

verse 19
> Woe to <u>THOSE</u> who are with child!
> Woe to <u>THOSE</u> who nurse children in those days!

verse 20
> Pray that <u>YOUR</u> flight be not in the winter and neither on a <u>SABBATH</u> day!

verse 23
> Then if any man shall say unto <u>YOU</u>, Lo here is Christ or there---believe it not!

verse 25
> Behold I have told <u>YOU</u> before!

verse 26
> Wherefore if they shall say unto <u>YOU</u>---
> Behold He is in the desert, etc.

Thus, one must conclude that this context ties us down to the days of the apostles---those to whom Christ was speaking in the text---not to some far away day or days of the future!

II <u>Notice again that some argue that these verses must speak of the Second Coming of Christ for several reasons</u>!

They say 24:14 makes it clear that the gospel must first be preached to all the world for a witness to all nations before the events of this chapter can take place, and that had not taken place in the time of the apostles. So that puts the context of this passage in the hour of Christ's Second Coming and not in the days of the apostles, because even to our day the gospel has not been preached to all the world---all nations.

But if we will look carefully at the following verses, which speak of the spread of the gospel in the first century, it might surprise us that these verses are in the Bible.

Colossians 1:23---Paul speaks of---
the hope of the gospel---which you have heard--- and which was preached <u>to every creature that is under heaven...</u>!

Romans 1:8---Paul tells the Romans---
Your faith is spoken of through out <u>the whole world</u>!

Romans 10:18---Paul says again---
But I say, Have they not heard? Yes, verily their sound went <u>into all the earth and their words unto the end of the earth</u>! (sounds and words of the gospel)

Romans 16:25-26---Paul says again---
....my gospel and the preaching of Jesus Christ.... <u>now is made manifest.....and made known to ALL NATIONS</u> for the obedience of the faith!

This is not to say that we do not have the same Great Commission today, but it is to note that Matthew 24:14 was fulfilled in the early era of the church. This gospel was preached in all the world for a witness to all nations. And after that first century of world evangelization, Christ could then come at any time. One is sadly mistaken if they say that Christ cannot come today because our world has never been evangelized.

After further discussion we nailed down several truths in summary.

1. The context of verses 4-28 is not our present day, but it is clearly the context of the early church in the first century!

2. The New Testament states that the world was evangelized in the first century, and that is not a necessity in our day before Christ can come, though we must acknowledge the Great Commission is still the mandate of our Lord's church for today!

3. I sensed the need, perhaps, to say a few more words concerning verses 26-28---

26 Wherefore, if they shall say unto <u>YOU</u>, Behold, he is in the desert, go not forth! Behold, he is in the secret chambers, believe it not! 27 For as the lightening cometh out of the east and shines even unto the west, so shall the coming of the Son of man be! 28 For wherever the carcass is, there will the eagles be gathered together.

> Note the pronoun <u>you</u> which sets it in the NT days!
> Note they are not to believe that Christ has come
> back literally! 26
> Note Christ's coming is a coming for judgment---
> and it will be a swift judgment, but not
> necessarily His literal second coming! 27
> Note again that as the gathering of vultures shows
> there is a carcass nearby, so these signs will
> show (according to the context) that the fall
> of Jerusalem is near! 28

We closed our study for this day, and I so wanted to ask Billy about Susie Belle, but he seemed to be antsy to leave for some reason. After he had shot out of our study in such a hurry, we had prayer for him and for Susie Belle, but little did we realize what was going on behind the scenes. That surprise came to us the next day, when Billy called me to tell us that he and Susie Belle were getting married in two weeks. This put an exposure of Susie Belle and her reason to marry Billy on the front burner. I called Mrs. Cardieux to see if she had received the information of the coming marriage, and she was somewhat shocked, as she had not heard about it. We all agreed it had to be the work of her brothers.

I decided that I would call Mac Turnover, who was owner and head of the Turnover News Agency, one of the largest news agencies of the nation. Mac came to know the Lord earlier through our ministry, and he had been ever so grateful, in that he could not do enough for us in the succeeding years. It was not that I wanted him to run a story on Billy or Susie Belle in his paper, but I knew he had his ways to gain information quietly concerning most any subject, even by sending a reporter in undercover to gather information one could not get in any other manner. He said he would look into this girl Susie Belle and Billy to see what he might learn---just some clear and objective facts about her and what her motive might be in marrying Billy.

Mac called me back in the next few days and sure enough, he had found out that Susie Belle McCoy was a plant by Billy's uncles, so they could regain their control of Billy. He would marry this girl, and she would give him a fit until he was back under the control of his wily uncles concerning his money and ministry. She would get a large cut of the money for a number of years, when the marriage failed. By that time we would no longer be around, and the brothers would have their clutches firmly embedded once again on Billy and his ministry and his money---just as we had guessed. I had marveled many times at the ability of Mac Turnover to get information for me, and I really wondered how he did it. I had never asked him exactly about his sources, but I knew his information was true, for his accuracy had never failed me---he always got the information right.

When I got off the phone, I could only shake my head and say to myself, "Billy, Billy, Billy. What in the world have you gotten yourself into now. And how will we ever get you out of this? And further, how could a young man be so blessed with an ability to preach the Word of God, and yet be so simple and blind concerning girls?" I had wondered several times why some excellent preachers I had known, had never shown the gift of "discernment" either, when it came to the young ladies. One mistake in that area, whether it be a stupid marriage or a stupid encounter with some tempting Jezebel---and one's ministry could be over.

My prayer was that we would not be too late in our efforts to save poor Billy from the clutches of the great enemy, the devil, as he does seek to ruin us all in the Christian life, and especially ministers in some way during their ministry.

Chapter 14

Billy seemed his good-old-boy self, as we gathered for our next study, and soon we were in up to our necks in the phrase found in Matthew 24:29, which says, *Immediately after the tribulation of those days...*certain things happened. I asked them to remember what we had studied in our last hour, and we named the events mentioned in Matthew 24:4-28, events we had seen were clearly going to take place soon in the days of the apostles---days of tribulation and sorrow during the fall of Jerusalem.

Then our text says, *Immediately after the tribulation of those days...!* I asked them again to remember our last study, which showed clearly that verses 4-28 of Matthew 24 were speaking of the days of the fall of Jerusalem and the temple and not of the latter days of our times. I then read to them a heading from a well-known Bible, which introduced this section with the words, *The King's Return to Earth at the Close of the Tribulation!* This means that the one writing the headings in this Bible, from which I had read, saw the next events as Christ's return to earth at the end times, following a tribulation period at that hour also. But how can one interpret it in this manner, when the text clearly says that *Immediately after the tribulation of those days*, those days being the fall of Jerusalem and the chaos of that hour, which we had just seen clearly described in the context of the days of the apostles?

I told them I wanted us to look carefully at those key words to see if they could mean anything else except, *Immediately after the tribulation of those days* (the days just described by our Lord concerning the fall of Jerusalem), which would put "those days" in the first century and not in the 20th or 21st century or any other future century beyond the first century.

Immediately---euthos

This is an adverb which means straightway,

immediately or forthwith and it can also mean shortly or very soon. So there is no question about the timing set forth here---what takes place from verse 29 onward is the same context of verses 4-28.

after---meta

Used with the accusative it speaks of sequence or the order in which one thing follows another---such as---after.

the tribulation---thlipsis

meaning affliction or tribulation or distress or oppression.

of those days---hameron ekeinon

meaning exactly what it says---the tribulation of those days of the first century just described in Matthew 24:4-28. The demonstrative pronoun is used here which is a reference to a thing previously mentioned or implied or already familiar.

I know it may sound redundant, but the passage clearly means---after the affliction of the days Christ has just described---the Jews fleeing Jerusalem, etc. We must say again that this is something in the first century and not in the 20th or 21st century. What has caused men to place this event in the far future is what follows in verses 30-31, which does seem to be a picture of the Second Coming of Christ, when it says---

verse 30

Then will appear the sign of the Son of man in heaven and then shall all the tribes of the earth mourn, and they shall see the Son of man coming in the clouds of heaven with power and great glory!

verse 31

And He shall send His angels with a great sound of a trumpet, and they shall gather together his elect

71

from the four winds from one end of heaven to the other.

But should not this cause us to ask some questions in light of the whole of the context prior to these verses, which spoke so clearly of the first century destruction of Jerusalem, and of the phrase telling us these next things happen "immediately after the tribulation and affliction of those days," speaking of the first century? Surely it would take an unimaginable twist of our hermeneutics (principles of Bible study and interpretation) to make verses 30-31 to all of a sudden now speak of our last days and the second coming of Christ, when that which was previously described was the fall of Jerusalem. And even this section begins with a gigantic cataclysmic manifestation of God's power at this hour of the destruction of Jerusalem.

The sun shall be darkened! 29

The moon shall not give its light! 29

The stars shall fall from heaven! 29

The powers of heaven shall be shaken! 29

The sign of the Son of man will appear in heaven! 30

Then all of the tribes of the earth will mourn! 30

The tribes of earth shall see the Son of man coming
    in the the clouds of heaven with power and great
      glory! 30

And Christ shall send His angels with a great sound
    of a trumpet and they will gather together His elect
    from the four winds---from one end of heaven
    to the other! 31

I told them again, that because context is king, this must speak of the days of the first century and not our days or future days to come in our future history. Thus, the proper question was, how can this passage be speaking of the

Second Coming of Christ? Is it not speaking of the destruction of Jerusalem, as clearly seen in its CONTEXT?

This is not to say there will be no Second Coming of Christ or that the Second Coming of Christ has already taken place. But it is to say that the context of this passage rules out the possibility of taking this passage as speaking of Christ's Second Coming. There are other passages that speak of Christ's Second Coming, when our Lord does come back again in power and great glory in the future.

The question then becomes, what is this passage saying? We have seen its context ties us to the first century AD and to the fall of Jerusalem! But what does it mean and how do we interpret it as it applies to that first century period of time, rather than to the latter days of our history? I told Billy that would be his assignment for our next hour of study---to see if he could find the meaning of verses 29-31 in light of the context we had seen in the previous verses of Matthew 24.

After we had prayed, Billy, began to tell us what a wonderful girl Susie Belle was. She was so unselfish and so helpful to him, that he could not have asked for a more spiritual girl. And then he hit us again with the bombshell---though we knew it already---they were getting married the next weekend---a week from today. And they wanted me and Dink to marry them.

Thus, the day of Armageddon had come, as far as Billy was concerned, and it would be next weekend, and there seemed to be nothing we could do about it. We tried even after our Bible study on this day, to talk Billy out it it, but he then became belligerent and defensive, and it was obvious, that no one could talk him out of marrying Susie Belle now. It was God's will, he said, and they were going to be married, whatever we said. Then he walked out in a huff, though none of us had agreed to the marriage.

Chapter 15

When Billy walked out on us so rudely, we decided to stay over a day or so and try to see him again. When I called him the next day, I had no idea how he would react to any further attempt to talk to him. His response at first, when finally I got him on the phone, was somewhat cold, but then he agreed to meet with me and Dink and discuss the matter further. Again, I was glad we were not flying a commercial airline, which meant we could stay here as long as necessary to help him understand what he was doing, if he married Suzie Belle. We had our Learjet waiting, but it would go no where till we were ready to depart. I told Dink later I thought I might buy one of those Learjets, but I was only kidding, especially when I heard how much one cost---a new one started at five million dollars or more! But that humor would have to wait, because right now we knew not what we might face in exposing Susie Belle further to Billy.

And Billy did show up at the appointed hour, and after a few words of stiff but friendly talk and smiles and a little joking around, I addressed the problem before us, when I asked Billy how well he really knew Susie Belle. He began to bubble all over the place again, which almost made me wish I had started somewhere else on the subject. But then after a few statements of our assurance to him that we really loved and enjoyed helping him, I stated our concern with a question.

"Billy, you haven't known Susie very long, have you?"

He nodded his head in agreement!

"And Billy, you don't know much about her, do you?"

And he had to agree again, but he added that he knew she was the girl for him. When I asked him how he knew she was the girl for him, he smiled a big smile, and said Jesus had led him to her, and Jesus would not make any mistakes. Then I wondered how I was ever going to convince him that idea could be wrong, not that Jesus was wrong, but that he was convinced Jesus agreed with him, and on that he was wrong---Jesus didn't agree!

And then I squared with him and told him that we had information that she was working with his uncles, so she too could get part of his money, and that her profession of faith was a false one, just for that purpose---to get his money. When I saw the look on his face, I was almost sorry I had said such a thing, but I knew we had to face the truth sooner or later---better now than later, when he was already married to her, and it would be too late to change things. Then I saw tears coming into his eyes, and he began to cry with open and engulfing sobs, such great sobs that he could not stop crying. I was surprised that he had not come back at us with some anger, but it was apparent that he was not mad at us, but his problem was a broken heart. I must admit, I have never felt so sorry for anyone in all my life. I handed him a handkerchief, and we could only wait for the sobs and deep breathing to stop, so we could see what his attitude really was in this situation.

When he finally spoke, he placed the blame on himself, as he said he probably could have guessed that, because no one but Jesus had ever loved him for who he was. And then he broke down and cried some more. I tried to assure him that God had the right girl waiting for him somewhere down the road in his life, IF it was God's will for him to marry. But that didn't seem to help him any. I asked Dink to pray for us, and when he had finished praying, I prayed, and we gave it all over to the Lord. Then when we had finished praying, he asked us how he could tell her what he knew, and I suggested that he just tell her he didn't think she was God's will for his life---no reason for details.

And, really, her reaction to this statement might be that which showed her true motive in wanting to marry him---

not because she loved him, but because she wanted something for herself. He agreed we would leave it all with "Jeeeeesus"---as he stated it, and "Jeeeeesus" would show us the truth in the matter. I told him to let her down gently and don't mention how he had come to know about her true motives or that he even knew of her true motives. Just tell her that he had become convinced their marriage was not God's will, and that he had to obey the Lord on this matter, and then see how she reacted and let us know.

After we prayed, we went our ways, and I wondered if he would see her that night or wait till a day or so had passed, or would he even get cold feet and not confront her at all? Time would tell! And if he did confront her, what would that cause his uncles to do---come after him and Dink and me again, blaming us for the ruination of their plans? At least his uncles had left us alone in peace and quiet, as they thought they had their problem solved by Susie Belle marrying Billy.

Before leaving for home I told Mrs. Cardieux of Billy's decision to stop the marriage. I suggested that she keep her eyes on this situation and give Billy any and all the help he might need, as he wrestled his way through this mess with Susie Belle and his uncles (her brothers). We warned her of the possibility that Billy might let her talk him out of the break-up, and if she heard anything to that effect, break-up or no break-up, let us know.

To my surprise, when I got to my office the next Monday, after this past weekend, I had some visitors waiting for me---the uncles and Susie Belle. And they were fighting mad! When I saw them there, I made a phone call to Dink (they didn't know who I was calling), and he was on the scene in a flash. I wanted Dink there not only for protection, but to confirm how they (even Susie Belle) reacted and treated me in the rage of this hour.

Chapter 16

It seemed very clear that someone had coached Susie Belle, as to how to react, when and if Billy would break up with her. Or else she was a very shrewd girl on her own, knowing she could not lose it and blow-up in a mad fit, which would show her real heart. She had to play the part of a crushed and rejected girl with a broken heart. I had to wonder, if Billy had fallen for her charades. But, quickly, on second thought, I had to conclude that Billy had truly rejected her, or she would not be here now bawling her eyes out, even though they might be crocodile tears. I decided I would listen to them and see if I could catch what they were up to now.

So while the uncles begged on her behalf (and their behalf, if the truth were known), and while she bawled her eyes out, I listened with great suspicion, looking for their next move. They said, if we would just go on with the wedding, they would bow out of managing Billy (they had already been thrown out of that responsibility), and they would just help Susie Belle guide Billy in his ministry, and that she and Billy would get all the money and have the final word on all things. I smiled, as I thought, that a blind man could have seen right through that one. If she managed the money, the uncles surely had made a deal with her that they would get a cut of Billy's money. Plus, with her managing the money, what chance did Billy have of ever managing his own ministry and finances? How dumb these people thought I must be, if I would fall for that scheme.

So I told them, this was not my decision, but Billy's. And then I asked what Billy had said about this? They then guaranteed me that Billy was in agreement with this arrangement, but somehow I just did not believe that either. I asked them further why they did not bring Billy with them, and they made up some kind of excuse that he was very busy today and could not come. I then thought that I would make one last stab at them, to see if I could rattle them out of their "nice-guys and nice girl" mode. So I asked why Billy could not be the one who managed the money. Their answer was that Billy was not skilled in that area of finances, and that is why they began helping him to begin with, which I doubted. Even if it might start that way, their being nice guys helping their nephew, it soon would get way out of control, as would any other arrangement they might seem to claim to submit to.

Finally, one of the uncles asked me to cooperate and suggest this plan to Billy, and I told him, "Absolutely not! Never ever under any circumstance at any time, any place or anywhere would I ever suggest Billy do that!" It was then that Mr. Nice Guys and Miss Weepy Eyes showed their true colors, as they (including Miss Weepy Eyes) began to cuss me out, calling me all kinds of horrible names, and even making threats against my life.

I told them they were on the campus of a Christian Seminary, and such language was not allowed, and if they persisted, I would be forced to call the campus police to escort them off of the premises or even put them in jail. When they persisted, Dink stepped in, and when one of them took a swing at him, he floored him. Thus, finally, with Dink's help and two of the campus police, they were escorted off campus and told never to come back.

As they left, all kinds of threats came from their foul mouths, as they erupted with vile curse words again. The worst language came from Miss Susie Belle, and when they were gone, I asked Dink if he thought Billy would believe us, when we told him what a foul-mouthed girl she was. Billy confirmed later that she had cussed him out, when he told her he had decided not to marry her. I wondered why then they even came to see me? And I was glad her foul mouth had convinced Billy of her treachery, just as we had warned.

Chapter 17

We heard no more from Susie Belle and Billy's uncles, but we spoke with Billy a few times, and all had been peaceful and quiet, after they were kicked off our campus. However, I wondered when the next explosion might take place. So it was with some concern that we traveled the next Saturday to the mountains. But Billy said the same thing, that there was nothing new nor any further words or bursts of madness from his uncles or Susie Belle. In fact he hadn't even seen or heard from any of them.

When we finally got around to our study of Matthew 24, I told them we needed a little review, before we could proceed. We had covered the first 28 verses of Matthew 24, and we had noted that it all pertained to the subject of the coming fall and destruction of Jerusalem in the first century A.D. We had given several reasons why that was so, but the strongest one was that in this section of Scripture Jesus used the personal pronoun "you" or "ye" in reference to His apostles, as the ones who would be facing that coming day of the various events around 70 A.D. when Jerusalem fell.

We had also called attention to the next section, as it began at verse 29 with the statement that "immediately" after the tribulation of "those days," which are words that clearly referred to those previous days of this context, which we had just discussed in verses 4-28 in relation to the fall of Jerusalem, and again not some far away days of centuries or millenniums. At this hour---the first century---

The sun is darkened! 29
The moon shall not give its light! 29
The stars shall fall from heaven! 29
The powers of heaven shall be shaken! 29
The sign of the Son of man will appear in heaven! 30
Then all of the tribes of the earth will mourn! 30

The the tribes of earth shall see the Son of man coming
in the the clouds of heaven with power and great
glory! 30
And Christ shall send His angels with a great sound
of a trumpet and they will gather together His elect
from the four winds---from one end of heaven
to the other! 31

Now there are several questions we must face in light of the context and the above statements. We have seen that the context is clearly the time of the fall of Jerusalem. So, we have two choices: (1) We can ignore the entire context of the fall of Jerusalem and see this section as the bold insertion of the literal Second Coming of Christ, which will take place years and years later. But would not such actions violate all we have ever learned about the importance of context---context being king? (2) Or we could ask humbly if there might be other verses or a verse in the Bible which might give us guidance in interpreting these verses before us in Matthew 24? Could it be that verses 30 and 31 speak of Christ coming in a non-visible manner in 70 AD to bring His kingdom to God's people in this very unique hour of God's judgment, when the city of Jerusalem is destroyed in 70 A.D.?

I wondered if we have ever considered Matthew 16:28ff as helpful in understanding these verses in Matthew 24, especially verses 30 and 31? John Gill says of Matthew 16:28 that the verse begins with a strong assertion (the act of recognizing the truth of something), as Christ says strongly and forcefully:

Verily, I say unto you, there be some standing here who will not taste death, <u>till they see the Son of Man coming</u> in His Kingdom!

Which is to say that Jesus said in Matthew 16:28 that some were standing with Him that very day, as He spoke these words, while on earth, who would not die until they saw the Son of man coming in His kingdom. Which is to say also that Christ's kingdom would come in some manner in the first century A.D! John Gill says further then that this hour spoken of, as being in the first century, surely is not to be understood that Christ was speaking of His personal coming in the last days, when He would come to judge the quick and the dead at that final hour. Gill acknowledges further that some have thought this---that some not tasting death spoke of the hour of His glorious transfiguration, which account follows in Matthew 17. But Gill says that the hour of His transfiguration, at most, was but an emblem and a pledge of His future glory, rather than the appearance of His kingdom in some manner in great glory and power following His resurrection, when the gospel had been preached all over the world!

Gill concludes that the statements in Matthew 24:30-31 (and I would add Matthew16:28) can only have reference to the hour when Christ comes, not literally but in His great regal power, to show His authority in the destruction of the city of Jerusalem and the destruction of His enemies the Jews, who said, "Let His blood be upon us and our children!" And it is certainly true that there were some standing with Him that day in Matthew 16:28, who also saw the destruction of Jerusalem, which also exemplified the coming of His kingdom. Yes, His enemies in that hour of His coming in power, were at that time slain before Him, not by His literal presence, but by His power and authority, when Jerusalem fell. And surely this was the hour that a number of His disciples saw that destruction, and this is the fulfillment of the promise that they would not taste death until they saw the Son of Man coming in His kingdom, which too was at the hour of the destruction of Jerusalem and the temple, not a literal kingdom, but a spiritual one. Multitudes of the Jews of the city of Jerusalem were destroyed along with the city itself. It is then that the following took place---remember the setting---it is immediately after the tribulation of those days---immediately after the fall of Jerusalem---at the hour of Christ coming in His invisible kingdom.

1. Earthly and heavenly upheavals which sober men!
    The sun is darkened---what a fearful hour! 29
    The moon does not give its light---darkness! 29
    The stars shall fall from heaven---calamity! 29
    The powers of heaven shall be shaken! 29

2. Christ is mentioned along with the tribes of the earth!
    verse 30
    We are told that the sign of the Son of man will appear in heaven! This is not a trumpet which sounds, but it is the "sign" of the Son of man appearing in heaven at this hour! Whatever the sign is, it will be clear to the Jews that this is the sign of Christ, as they see it in the heavens! The Jews had continually badgered Christ to give them a sign, and He gave them many signs, but they were never satisfied or convinced, as they were blind to all His signs! This will be a sign they cannot deny, whatever it is---as it appears at the time of the fall of Jerusalem!
    verse 30
    We are told that the tribes of the earth shall mourn, which seems to be clearly a statement concerning the Jews in the land of Judea, for as Gill says, the other lands and countries were not usually divided

into tribes, as were the Jews! And neither were the other countries affected with the calamities and desolations of this hour, as were the Jews, for the vengeance of the Son of man is upon them!

verse 30

We are told again that the tribes of earth shall see the Son of man coming in the clouds of heaven with power and great glory! In light of the context, we would not take this coming as a literal coming, but what the Jews see in the clouds of heaven is His power and presence as judgment falls upon them, and they know it is from Him! Remember the context again, which does not allow us to move this coming in the clouds of heaven to the final Second Coming of our Lord! Plus, the Bible is full of statements that speak of His coming, but they are not always speaking of a literal coming!

For instance---

Revelation 2:5

Remember therefore from whence thou art fallen, and repent, and do the first works; or else I WILL COME UNTO THEE QUICKLY, and will remove thy candlestick out of his place, unless thou repent (not a literal coming).

Revelation 2:16---to the church of Pergamos!

Repent or else I WILL COME to thee quickly!

Plus several others of this nature---not literal!

Genesis 18:21

I WILL GO DOWN and see....! (not literal)

Deuteronomy 33:2

THE LORD CAME FROM SINAI AND HE CAME WITH TEN THOUSANDS OF SAINTS! (not literal)

See also--the following verses--not literal comings--
>Isaiah 31:4--the Lord of hosts shall <u>come down</u>!
>Isaiah 64:3---Thou <u>camest down</u>...!
>Isaiah 66:15---The Lord <u>will come</u> with fire, etc.
>Psalm 18:9---He bowed the heavens and <u>CAME DOWN</u>!
>Psalm 50:3---God shall <u>come</u> and not keep silence!
>Psalm 96:13---He <u>cometh</u> to judge the world!
>Psalm 144:5---Bow the heavens, O Lord, and <u>come down</u>!
>Hosea 8:1---He <u>shall come</u> as an eagle against the house of the Lord!
>Micah 1:3-4---The Lord <u>cometh forth</u> out of His place and <u>will come down</u> and tread on the high places of the earth!

Several others have noted, that if the writers of the Old Testament (and of the New Testament) used such symbolic language concerning the actions of God, is it not likely that the writers of the New Testament and the Lord Jesus Himself might use the same kind of imagery to describe events of such historic proportions as the destruction of Jerusalem?

3. Christ shall send His angels with a great sound of a trumpet and they will gather together His elect from the four winds--from one end of heaven to the other! 31

If all we had were verses 30 and 31 of Matthew 24, there could be a strong argument that this is the Second Coming of Christ. But since we have a full context of Matthew 24, we say again that this cannot be the context of the Second Coming, for the context ties us to the events mentioned previously, which are from the first century history of Christianity and what follows. As we interpret this passage, then, we must remember the statement which says that these events take place "immediately after the tribulation of those days," that is, after the horrible events of the fall of Jerusalem, which includes a period of about three years, including the time prior to the fall in 70 AD and then the fall itself. Thus, this passage takes place following the fall of Jerusalem, as the times of the Gentiles began with the final fall of Jerusalem, and God sent His messengers (the Greek word for angels can mean angels or even messengers). These angels or messengers herald that the great news of the gospel is now open to the Gentiles and God's messengers or preachers of the gospel, will go out to all the world to spread the good news of Christ.

As Adam Clark notes, the rebellious and obstinate Jews are now replaced in God's plan by the Gentiles, who are the elect of that hour, something which was predicted by our Lord in Matthew 8:11-12 and Luke 13:28-29 and a number of other places in the gospels. The children of the kingdom, that is the Jews, who were born with a legal right to the kingdom, but had now finally forfeited that right by their sin, are now thrust out. And it is true that the Christian message spread among the Gentiles and prevailed mightily after this period, and nothing contributed more to the success of the gospel, than the destruction of Jerusalem. It was at this hour that the kingdom of Christ was revealed and established in every part of the world of that day among the Gentiles.

Thus, we would conclude that this is the hour when Christ sends His messengers, after the fall of the city

85

of Jerusalem to the Gentiles, and He gathers them by the four winds (by---the preposition ek in the Greek), which can speak of the means or the instrument of gathering or the efficient cause of the gathering) from the uttermost part of earth to the uttermost part of heaven. Obviously, there is some symbolic language here, such as "gathered by the four winds" and "uttermost part of earth and heaven!" This symbolic language surely speaks of our Lord saving Gentiles in this age---saving Gentiles from every tribe and nation---far and wide and worldwide.

I apologized to my brothers for taking so long on this study, but I think they understood the reason for it. And after a time of discussion, we had prayer and closed our study time together. But then Billy brought something up, which completely surprised us again. He asked if it would be okay for him to have a date with Susie Belle's sister. I about dropped my teeth on that one, and they weren't even false teeth. My next question was direct, as I asked Billy how he ever got mixed up now with Susie Belle's sister, when he had such problems with Susie Belle herself?

He tried to tell us she was really a godly girl, who loved the Lord, and wasn't anything like her sister. With a smile I asked if Susie Belle had any other sisters, who might be next in line, if this present sister bombed out too. Then with love and grace we tried to explain to Billy that this might be another scam, being pushed by his two uncles and Susie Belle. And if it was a scam, then he would have four people coming after him to get his money.

It was then that he guaranteed us she was not like the other sister, but was truly a sweet and humble and godly girl! She knew all the books of the Bible and could name each one of them. She could even name all the apostles, too, another supposed positive for her. And she had a beautiful singing voice, something which Billy thought every preacher's wife should have, I guessed. But then he really got me, when he said that she knew theology better than he did, and she had been teaching him all about that area of study. When I asked him what Susie Belle thought of his new friendship with her sister, he said quietly, Susie Belle didn't know about them---yet.

As Dink and I flew home, we couldn't get over it. Billy never had a girl-friend in his life, but now in the last few weeks, he had latched on to two different girl-friends---one a scoundrel and the other her sister. And who knew what kind of girl she really was? She was probably another plant by the other three scoundrels---his uncles and Susie Belle. And what a simple naive boy Billy was---talk about stupidity or naivety. When I got home I called Mrs. Cardieux to see if she knew anything about it, but she was more ignorant and surprised about it than we were. Billy had told us that her name was Liza Lou McCoy.

I hated to do it, but I just had to call Mac Turnover and get his help again. With some laughter, he agreed to do so. In a few days we were given a report on Liza Lou McCoy---there was no such girl nor sister---at least not one named Liza Lou McCoy. And don't think that didn't send up bad vibes concerning Liza Lou! How many more similar tricks would they try and not expect to get caught immediately. What a clan this was---the thievery of the two uncles and the greed of Susie Belle, and now the stupidity of Liza Lou---the girl who claimed to be a theologian. I laughed as I brought Dink up to date on the whole mess.

And poor Billy---he may have had the gift of preaching, but he definitely did not have the gift of picking out a girl-friend or a wife from all the girls in the world. He might be a great preacher, but he had very poor spiritual insight when it came to girls!

Chapter 18

As usual, the time passed quickly, and on Saturday, we headed for the mountains, again. We had heard nothing more about Billy and his new girl friend. But when we got to Mrs. Cardieux's house, we were very surprised to find out that Billy had brought her to our study for that day. Seems like they were going somewhere, as soon our study was over. I must confess that a plan began to form in my mind, whereby we might entrap Liza Lou during our study, concerning her great claim to be steeped in theology. I prayed God would guide us, and even expose her before Billy, without our looking mean in the process.

As I taught I tried to see if Liza Lou was listening and comprehending what I was teaching, and I must admit that she seemed completely snowed by the subject. And to be honest, she was in a difficult place, jumping into the middle of our study. I concluded this might not be the best way to test her theology, but I decided I would seek to open the door for her to show her wisdom in theology or to show her ignorance without embarrassing her.

Our subject was the parable of the fig tree which is just four verses, so I read them out loud for their remembrance.

32 Now learn a parable of the fig tree! When its branch is yet tender and puts forth leaves, ye know that summer is near! 33 So likewise, ye, when ye shall see all these things, now it is near, even at the doors. 34 Verily I say unto you, This generation shall not pass, till all these things be fulfilled! 35 Heaven and earth shall pass away, but my words shall not pass away.

I told them again the importance of remembering the context, and that we cannot just jump into the middle of a section and put what is said in some new section in a different context from the whole, unless there is some clear and proper reason for doing so. Thus, we have seen that the context all through this chapter has been the fall of Jerusalem, and there is no clear reason to adopt a different context, as we enter this parable of the fig tree. We will take the thoughts of this section one by one and see how Jesus spoke here to the apostles.

Now you (apostles)---learn a parable of the fig tree! 32
You (pl) know summer is near when its branch is tender
    and brings forth leaves! 32
So likewise---you (pl) apostles---when you (pl) shall
    see all these things---then know it is near and even
        at the door! 33
Verily, I (Jesus) say unto you (pl---the apostles)---
    This (present) generation shall not pass away
        till all these things be fulfilled!
Heaven and earth shall pass away, but my words shall
    not pass away!

1. It cannot be denied that Jesus is still speaking to His apostles of the first century AD---take note of the words "you" and "ye" used in these verses!

2. It cannot be denied that Jesus wants His apostles to know this parable of a fig tree---it is addressed to them!

3. When the fig tree's branch is yet tender and puts forth its leaves, "ye" (Christ speaking to His apostles) know that summer is near!

4. Jesus speaking again says, So likewise (you apostles) when you shall see all these things that Christ has been talking about (which is the coming of the destruction of Jerusalem and God's punishment and rejection of the

Jews), then know what Christ has been talking about (the destruction of Jerusalem, etc.) is even at the doors!

5. Jesus speaking says, Verily or truly, this present generation (the generation of the first century before the fall of Jerusalem) shall not pass till all these things be fulfilled!

I am sorry to say that one well-known Bible says in a footnote that the word "generation" here, though commonly used in Scripture of those things living at that time, could not mean here those alive at the time of Christ, as none of these things in this text occurred then. Which means, I suppose, that all the events of Matthew 24 will yet occur in the latter days and and none of them occurred in the time of Christ! My answer must be, that nothing could be further from the truth. We have just seen how these events did take place in the first century, as the text clearly speaks of this generation---the generation of Christ and the apostles.

6. Jesus then concludes by saying that heaven and earth will pass away, but His words shall not pass away!

This is a confirmation statement of the full and complete and absolute accuracy of His words regarding that which He has been dealing with in the 24th chapter of Matthew. And if His words shall not pass away, we are better off if we understand them correctly, rather than making up our own minds concerning what is being said by our Lord. And remember, context is king! It is on this basis that we would conclude that this chapter speaks of the fall of Jerusalem and the judgments which took place at that hour, and though there is coming a further judgment of this world in the future, that is not the subject of this chapter or context!

After some further discussion, and when I saw we were near the closing hour I turned and addressed Liza Lou. I did not want to be mean or embarrass her, but I just had to find out something about her and her supposed knowledge of theology. Everyone had participated in our discussions during this hour, except her. So I thought I would give her an opportunity to contribute without embarrassing her, if she was so knowledgeable, as she had claimed to be.

I first asked her who her favorite theologian was!
Her answer was, "Oh, I read them all!"
My answer was, with a smile, "Oh, that's good!"
I then asked, "Are you familiar with Charles Hodge?"
And her answer was, "Yes, I have read him some!"
I then asked, "Which theology book is the best, in your opinion?"
And her answer was, "Oh, they are all good!"
Then I asked her, "Have you read Albert Schweitzer's theology book? And her answer was the same, that she had read parts of his book, but not all of it!
I decided I had asked her enough questions, and she had given me only general answers to my basic questions---she knew very little about theology and had read little, if any, in any theology book, and she did not know that Albert Schweitzer had never written a theology book. In fact he was a heretic, who had no faith in Jesus Christ as Lord or Savior! His basic book was to show Christ was fooled concerning His thoughts of Who He was and why He had come to this earth.

Now the question was, how do we tell Billy that she too is a fake? Will that boy ever learn? Maybe someone just needed to tell him clearly and bluntly to sit down and wait on God to bring along the right girl, something he had been doing till we came along and stirred up his uncles to enlist these girls to go after him to get his money for them and for his uncles. As things were going now, he just might marry the wrong girl---the one of his choice and not the girl of God's choice. This is what I thought about and prayed about all the way home that late afternoon. Somehow the Lord will have to intervene in this situation or Billy never will get through his early days of youth without wrecking his life and ministry. He was learning something about Bible study and exegesis and preaching, hopefully, but he didn't seem to know anything about girls---even though he had, so it seemed, a multitude of them after him now.

I finally got home in the early evening, and I had no sooner sat down, than the phone rang, and it was Billy. He asked me what I thought of Liza Lou, and I asked him if he really wanted to know, and he said yes. So I asked him a series of questions!

1. Is it true that she claims to be a sister to Susie Belle, when they really are not sisters?

2. Is it really true that she loves to read theology, when she thinks Albert Schweitzer wrote a theology book, when he didn't, but rather he was a heretic?

3. Could it be that she has the same motive for dating you, as did Susie Belle and as did your uncles in wanting to govern your ministry?

Then I shocked him when I told him bluntly that he had better be careful or he would be right back where he was with his uncles and Suzy Belle, if he was not already there!

Chapter 19

The next week was a busy one again, but we heard nothing from the mountains or Billy or Mrs. Cardieux. As the old saying goes, no news is good news, hopefully. I wondered sometimes if that was really true, as I prayed for Billy and his whole situation. All through the week, I also wondered if Liza Lou could influence him to do something stupid, like getting married, without letting us know. I was convinced that I needed to confront Billy again on this matter this coming Saturday, after we had met for study. So it was with some uncertainty that we flew to the mountains to meet once again with Billy for study.

Billy said nothing about Liza Lou before our study began, and neither did we ask him about her or any of his uncles or Susie Belle. Hopefully, they all had stopped bugging Billy, but that might be too much to hope for. I had decided I would handle this study a little differently by asking questions that Billy should be able to answer as he remembered the context of the 24th chapter of Matthew. We were going to cover verses 36-39, which said---

36 But of that day and hour knoweth no man, no, not the angels of heaven, but my Father only. 37 But as the days of Noah were, so shall also the coming of the Son of man be. 38 For as in the days before the flood they were eating and drinking, marrying and giving in marriage, until the day that Noah entered into the ark, 39 And knew not until the flood came, and took them all away, so shall also the coming of the Son of man be!

Question One---

I asked Billy what the phrase "that day and hour that no man knoweth" referred to in verse 36? And what is the context of the phrase "that day?" Billy noted that surely the phrase "that day and hour which no man knoweth, not even the angels of heaven, but only the Father" must, context-wise, refer us back to the parable just stated, as it continues to speak of the fall of Jerusalem, and that no man knew the exact day nor hour that would be. Contextually, he said, it could not be referring to the Second Coming of Christ, but it was referring to the fall of Jerusalem.

Question Two

Verse 37 likens this hour to the days of Noah, and that the coming of the Son of man is like those days of Noah. According to the context, what is the meaning of the coming of the Son of man?

Billy said that this was too easy, or maybe I was a good teacher. According to the context, this had to be referring, not to the Second Coming of Christ but to the judgment coming at the fall of Jerusalem in 70 AD, for the days of Noah too were days of judgment.

Question Three

Give your explanation of verse 38 and how it applies to the time frame in which it is set.

Billy again couldn't smile enough, as he was with me all the way, as he said, "Just as in Noah's days before the flood, they were eating and drinking and marrying and giving in marriage, until the day that Noah entered into the ark, and so it will be even up to the day of the destruction of Jerusalem. They will be doing the same, when Titus and his army comes against Jerusalem."

Question Four

Verse 39 continues to say they knew not till the flood

94

came and took them all away, so also shall be the coming of the Son of man. What coming of the Son of man does this passage refer to according to the context?

Billy was ready again, and he told me it was like picking apples off of an apple tree. This was not the Second Coming of Christ at the end of time, but this was the coming of the Son of man at the destruction of Jerusalem, according to the context, though some have tried to make it the coming of Christ in the end times.

Thus, I summarized verse 36, saying this passage cannot be what some have called a "divisional passage" in Matthew 24 which divides the earlier part of this chapter from the latter part of the chapter. Or to put it another way, it cannot be that verse 36 here divides Chapter 24 into two parts. This would be saying that verses 1-35 speak of the fall of Jerusalem, while verses 36-51 speak of the Second Coming of Christ. Not so, for this is all the same context.

I pointed out that many have sought to divide Matthew 24 in this manner, but such a procedure has two basic problems. Problem one is that the various authors cannot agree as to what verse is the divisional verse, and thus they seek to divide the chapter in various places as the dividing line between the fall of Jerusalem and the Second Coming of Christ. Note the following different places where different scholars have sought to make a divisional verse---

Some say 24:29 is the divisional verse!
Some say 24:33 is the divisional verse!
Some say 24:35 is the divisional verse!
Some say 24:36 is the divisional verse!
See *Biblical Apocalyptics* by Milton Terry, page 217.

Then I noted a second problem with dividing Matthew 24 into two divisions, part of it speaking of the fall of Jerusalem and the other part speaking of the Second Coming of Christ. Take note of the fact that the phrases which mention the "coming of the Son of man" are in both the first half of the chapter, which some say refers to the fall of Jerusalem, and also in the second half of the chapter, which some say refers to the Second Coming of Christ. See the examples as follow---

verse 27
   the coming of the Son of man!
verse 30
   the Son of man coming in the clouds of heaven!
verse 37
   the coming of the Son of man!
verse 39
   the coming of the Son of man!
verse 44
   the Son of man cometh!

Surely the usage of these similar phrases gives this whole section a continuity, whereby we cannot divide the section into various parts.

We discussed these verses for a length of time, and found we were amazed at how much Billy had learned thus far in our study. But then we turned to the shocking news brought to us by Billy, as we found out some things unknown to us previously. Billy had just learned that though "Mountain Man" McCoy was not the father of Liza Lou (shock number one), yet he had taken her into his house several years ago, and the rumor was that she was something of a second wife to him, (shock number two), though he was old enough to be her father. We noted again that this was something Billy had not known when he began dating her, and he had just yesterday learned that he was in trouble with "Mountain Man" McCoy, for doing such a thing. Plus, Suzie Belle, it seems, to save her own neck, had told "Mountain Man" certain lies about Billy's behavior with her, when they were dating, and now he was insisting that Billy marry one of these girls, because of all the lies the girls had told about Billy and his supposed behavior with them. This put Billy in trouble with "Mountain Man's" daughter and also his kept girl, and he seemed to want some money for Billy's supposed transgressions against all of them---himself and his daughter and his younger lady friend.

I let out a deep breath, knowing we should have seen this coming, but it was too late now. Billy assured us that his actions with the two girls had been way above board--- always, He hadn't even kissed either one of them. In fact, he had never kissed any girl. He was that shy and that fearful of such a situation. All he lived for was the Lord and the preaching of His Word, and he was a complete rookie in the matter of a girl friend. Plus, they had him fooled that Susie Belle and Liza Lou were sisters.

At this serious moment, he broke down and cried and cried again, as he thought his ministry was finished, and that he could never prove their accusations were false. He wished he had never met these girls, or that he had never responded to their interest in him. That's how shy he was--- he never would have dated them, unless they had pursued him. He was convinced he would be a bachelor now for the rest of his life---if he lived through this problem with "Mountain Man" McCoy!

Then he asked me and Dink if we would go see Mountain Man, and Dink and I looked at each other, trying to think this whole thing through, and if this was needed at this hour. I could see in my mind the meeting of Mr. McCoy, "the Mountain Man," and Dink, "the former mafia man," and me---the "preacher man." Billy didn't help matters any, when he offered that we needed to be careful, because Mr. McCoy had a prison record, mostly for bootlegging in the mountains and for having crushed several men's skulls (figuratively speaking, I supposed or hoped) in fights over the years. The girls had told him that.

I didn't say it out loud, but I must admit my thoughts were saying, "Billy, Billy, Billy! How could you have been so stupid, as to get involved with this supposed family---two wild girls and a wild father, who wasn't the father of one of them?" I guess that showed just how naive he was, not only in his relationship with his thieving uncles, but even more so in the area of girls. Billy didn't say much, but just kept crying and wiping his eyes. All I could do was try to cheer him up, and so I smiled and reminded him of Psalm 118:6, which says, "*The Lord is on my side---I will not fear what can man do unto me!*

We prayed and then parted with the promise that Dink and I would see "Mountain Man" McCoy this coming week---the Lord willing. But that raised a lot of questions. When would we see him? Who would contact him, and what would we tell him, when the contact was made? Would he be open to see us and talk to us? Would he be trying to use this for some personal reason, such as some way to get his hands on Billy's money too? Would he be shooting straight with us, or would he be lying all over the place, just to pull off some scam of some sort with us with Billy as the fall guy. What if he began to spread false rumors about us all over the community, like he had done with Billy?

Such possibilities did not help a person to sleep at night, but it sure caused us to put it all before the Lord in prayer---continually.

Chapter 20

The next week flew by too fast, when one knew that during the next weekend we had to face Mountain Man McCoy. Billy had made the arrangements, and McCoy had agreed to meet with us. I suggested we meet at the church where he and his family attended, and I must admit, I wondered how often Mountain Man himself went to church in light of his reputation and past history. Before we got to the church, I told Billy to say nothing, and let Dink and I take care of it---no matter what they said or threatened against him, and even though it might look like we were giving in to them. When we got there we found out McCoy's pastor was present, also, at his insistence, but the question was---would be a help or a hindrance in our discussions?

The group was made up of Dink and me and Billy and Mountain Man and Pastor Sweet. I must admit that I hoped Pastor Sweet's demeanor matched his name and might even transfer in some manner over to Mountain Man himself. After a word of prayer by Pastor Sweet, Mountain Man took over the meeting, as he laid out several demands he had because of the supposed shameful actions of Billy Hill towards his two daughters, Susie Belle and Liza Lou. He called them his daughters, but we knew Liza Lou was not his daughter. The following charges were brought against Billy:

1. Billy had false intentions towards his daughters as he lied to them promising marriage--- something he never intended to carry out!
2. Billy had behaved immorally with his daughters as he had attacked them for his own purposes!
3. Billy made promises he never intended to keep--- such as money and a big house and a nice car for his girls!

Both the Mountain Man and Pastor Sweet spoke long and loud concerning these matters, and it seemed true that Pastor Sweet was in on the scheme also to get all he could from Billy too. I must admit that it looked dark and cloudy for Billy this day, as they told wild story after wild story about Billy and what he had supposedly done to these poor little innocent girls. And they made Billy out to be, not only the biggest playboy who had ever lived, but also the most immoral young man who had ever set foot on this earth. Finally, when they were finished, it was our turn. I asked them if there was any proof of what Billy had supposedly done, except for the accusations of the daughters? With this Mountain Man got even madder, telling us he had the word of his girls and that was enough. We then asked for a week to think over these accusations and to verify them and to decide then what we would be willing to do about their accusations against Billy.

And they certainly did not like this idea either---they wanted to get this over with as soon as possible for the sake of the girls, they said, and for the sake of their reputations, and probably more so in order to get their hands on the money, too. I asked them if we could speak to the girls, and they said, absolutely not, because the girls had suffered too much already. And then they threatened to take Billy to court over the whole matter, if we did not settle this today. When I asked them what they meant by "settling it today," they said that they would settle the matter today for no less than $50,000---today! If there was no settlement today, they would sue Billy for one million dollars, which would ruin his reputation, they said, as well as his ministry.

I must admit, I almost choked on that "million dollar" figure. And as I looked at Billy, he looked like he was about to die over this whole matter. But we had told him to let us handle it, and he was doing just that, except for the looks of death on his face.

100

It was then, as we had planned, that Dink took over, as he said, "Mistuh Mountain Man! How well does you'se know dose girls of yours? Has dey always told ya da truths? We'se gots some records of der arrests, right here, an' does you's wants ta see it? Seems ta me dey ain't been da nice little ladies dat you says dey are or tink dey are, accordin' to da police records? Lemme see here, dey was arrested fer immoral activities several times last year---an' I mean several times---an' dat was way before dey ever met Billy here! Deys even spent several nights in jail fer illegal drugs and several other times fer shopliften' of clothes from stores! Could it be dat dey is taken after der daddy, whose been in jail a number of times too?"

I took note that Dink's exposure of Mountan Man's girls left him fuming, and I began wondering how long he would let Dink go on like this.

"Sir, I realize we all is sinners an' in need of da Lord Jesus Christ, an' He alone can change our lives by His salvation, and then He helps us quit our lyin' an' cheaten' an' schemin' an' stealin' an' illegal druggin' an' immoral playin' around, like it seems you an' your girls an' Preacher Sweet here has been doin', cause he sure ain't a godly preacha, lyin' like he's doin' right now!"

It was here that Mountain Man got a strange look on his face, as he asked Dink, "What did you say your name was?" And the answer came back, "My name's Dink---jus' Dink. Its been dat since I was a kid an' even back in my days in da Mafia, an' ever since da Lord Jesus saved me."

Then Mountain Man got a big smile on his face, as he heard these words. He then told us he had heard of this fellow known as "Dink," when he was in prison. Dink, a little guy in size, who was supposed to be the biggest smart aleck ever, but few men had ever whipped him in a fight. As the discussion went on, it seemed the lure of a fight,

101

whereby Mountain Man could whip someone like Dink, who had a reputation for fighting, meant more to him than money or the defense of his girls supposed reputations. Thus, he put down his shot gun, and took off his shirt, and challenged Dink to try to whip him right now! Dink played it cool, at first, acting like he wanted nothing to do with McCoy, but finally he agreed, and the fight was on.

As far as size, Dink was outweighed by more than a hundred pounds, as Mountain Man had a large beer belly and big fists, but the big belly only meant Dink would have more speed and more mobility and more stamina, if the fight lasted very long. But if Mountain Man got in one good strong blow, it might all be over for Dink. As the fight unfolded, McCoy swung at Dink again and again, but never connected, as Dink moved quietly out of the range of each swing. After several minutes of that, it was clear that McCoy was tiring, and he was even frustrated, because he couldn't hit Dink, and Dink was fresh because he hadn't even taken a swing at Mountain Man. Finally, as quick as a cat, Dink took one mighty swing and not only floored Mountain Man, but he knocked him out cold.

Dink stood over him, and Preacher Sweet got some water and poured it on McCoy's face, and as he came to, Dink asked him if he wanted to continue the fight, and he said no. Then Dink asked if he wanted to continue the lies he and his girls were telling on Billy, and as he got to his feet, he said he would have to think on that, and Dink hit him again and knocked him cold a second time, because he had given the wrong answer. When he woke up again, after a few minutes, he grabbed his jaw, as if it was broken, and Dink asked him to tell the truth---unless he wanted more!

It was then that he admitted that they had been lying about Billy, and he knew that Billy hadn't even touched the girls, but he thought he had seen a way to make some money out of it. Dink looked at Preacher Sweet and asked him if that was true, and the preacher hung his head and admitted that he had been lying also, in order to get some of the money. Both agreed that their pursuit of Billy and his money was over---they would leave Billy alone. They then agreed to come with us to Mrs. Cardieux's home and tell her the same---that they had lied about Billy. We insisted that they do this so that we could be assured this whole thing was over and would be over for good, which they did.

Finally, when we were alone again with Billy, we cautioned him in no uncertain terms to be careful of the girls in the future, because he was a nice looking young man with a ministry that paid him well---well for mountain folk---and there would be many more young ladies, who he might not be able to trust. He guaranteed us that he had learned his lesson, and he was going to be a bachelor, unless the Lord hit him over the head in some way and told him that a certain young lady was God's choice for him.

Then Billy said something quite interesting, when he noted the providence of God at work in the events of the day, whereby the Mountain Man had been in prison, where someone had known Dink from his days in the mafia. Being one who was always looking for a fight with someone with a reputation, Mountain Man couldn't resist picking a fight with Dink. If that had not taken place, there is no telling what might have unfolded in the plan of McCoy to extort some money from them.

Billy marveled in God's providence in all these things. Meeting us! Our willingness to teach him! His split with his uncles! Learning so much about the Bible! I reminded him that God's sovereignty guides us through life, and we follow, and He sends in His time His choice of a mate for marriage, if marriage is His will for us. Billy agreed with the last thought---no more girls for him till the right one came along!

Chapter 21

We heard nothing more, after returning home on Saturday in our Learjet, nor did we hear anything the next week. Things seemed peaceful and quiet, not only on the home front (that is in our city), but also back on the battle-field in the mountains. We were praying for the whole thing to be quieted forever, even though Mountain Man had a bruised ego and might be trying to save his face before his buddies, who all by now had heard of his whipping by a smaller fellow named "Dink!"

As we began our study the next weekend, I decided we would begin with Matthew 24:42, a verse from our last study, and include then verses 43 and 44. The text then read as follows---

42 Watch therefore: for ye know not what hour your Lord doth come. 43 But know this, that if the goodman of the house had known in what watch the thief would come, he would have watched and would not have suffered his house to be broken up. 44 Therefore be ye also ready: for in such an hour as ye think not the Son of man cometh!

verse 42

The previous context has made it very clear that this is the hour of the coming of the Lord to destroy Jerusalem and not the Second Coming of Christ. It is clear that many will be taken by surprise and captured or they will be killed, while some may escape, as we have already seen.

verse 43

In light of what has just been said in verse 42, verse 43 is an illustration given to further alert the readers of the surprise of the hour of the coming destruction of Jerusalem. The illustration involves a man who has some responsibility for a house, maybe his own or maybe the house of another. If this man had known when the thief would come to rob the house, whatever the hour of the night it might be, he would have been watching and waiting and ready for the thief. He would not have allowed his house to have been robbed. Thus, the application of this short parable is this---simply that the Lord is coming to destroy Jerusalem, but no one knows the day nor the hour in its exactness. But those who are true believers are warned to be ready--they have been warned of the coming fall of Jerusalem.

verse 44

The simple admonition in light of what has previously been said and pictured in the parable is clearly this---"Therefore be ye also ready, for in an hour that you think not the Son of man cometh (comes to destroy Jerusalem)." Be prepared for that hour---the destruction of Jerusalem---for it will be a time of suddenness, when men are unaware, for whatever reason it might be. Then after the hour of destruction is come, no readiness can be made---it will be too late.

I told Dink and Billy that it was my desire for them to understand how devastating and destructive and unbearable the fall of Jerusalem was. Maybe then we could understand these strong and powerful warnings given by Christ to watch and be prepared for that hour of Jerusalem's fall. To help understand, I read to them the following words of Josephus, the Jewish historian, who was a captive of the Romans, and he was able to see the great horror of the destruction and fall of Jerusalem in 70 AD.

Throughout the city [Jerusalem], people were dying of hunger in large numbers, and enduring unspeakable

105

sufferings. In every house the merest kind of food sparked violence, and close relatives fell to blows, snatching from one another the pitiful supports of life. No respect was paid even to the dying; the ruffians [anti-Roman zealots] searched them, in case they were concealing food somewhere in their clothes, or just pretending to be near death. Gaping with hunger, like mad dogs, lawless gangs went staggering and reeling through the streets, battering down the doors like drunkards, and so bewildered that they broke into the same house two or three times in an hour. Need drove the starving to gnaw at anything. Refuse, which even animals rejected, was collected and turned into food. In the end they were eating belts and shoes, and the leather stripped off their shields. Tufts of withered grass were devoured, and sold in little bundles for four drachmas.

But why dwell on the commonplace rubbish which the starving were driven to feed upon, given that which I have to recount in an act unparalleled in the history of either the Greeks or the barbarians, and as horrible to relate as it is incredible to hear? For my part I should have gladly omitted this tragedy, lest I should be suspected of monstrous fabrication. But there were many witnesses of it among my contemporaries; and besides, I should do poor service to my country if I were to suppress the agonies she went through.

Among the residents of the region beyond Jordan was a woman called Mary, daughter of Eleazar, of the village of Behthezuba (the name means "House of Hyssop"). She was well off, and of good family, and had fled to Jerusalem with her relatives, where she became involved with the siege. Most of the property she had she packed up and brought with her from Peraea, but it had been plundered by the tyrants [Simon and John, leaders of the Jewish war-effort], and the rest of her treasure together with such foods as she had been able to procure, was being carried off by their henchmen in their daily raids. In her bitter resentment the poor woman cursed and abused these extortioners, and this incensed them against her. However, no one put her to death either from exasperation or pity. She grew weary of trying to find food for her kinfolk. In any case, it was by now impossible to get any food, wherever you tried. Famine gnawed at her vitals and the fire of rage was ever fiercer than famine. So driven by fury and want, she committed a crime against nature. Seizing her child, an infant at the breast, she cried, *"My poor baby, why should I keep you alive in this world of war and famine? Even if we live till the Romans come* (this was a time of siege), *they will make slaves of us; and anyway, hunger will get us before slavery does, and the rebels are crueler than both. Come, be food for me, and an avenging fury to the rebels, and a tale of cold horror to the world to complete the monstrous agony of the Jews."* With these words she killed her son, roasted the body, swallowed half of it, and stored the rest in a safe place. But the rebels were on her at once, smelling roasted meat, and threatening to kill her instantly, if she did not produce it. She assured them she had saved them a share and then she revealed the remains of her child. Seized with horror, they all stood paralyzed at the sight. But she said, *"This is my own child, and my own handiwork. Eat for I have eaten already. Do not show yourselves weaker than a woman, or more pitiful than a mother. But if you have the pious scruples and shrink away from human sacrifice, then what I have eaten can count as your share, and I will eat what is left as well."* At that they slunk away, trembling, not daring to eat, although they were reluctant to yield even this food to the mother. The whole city soon rang with the abomination. When people heard it they shuddered, as though they had done it themselves.

Could it be that scenes like this, and there were many, could have been the results of many people not listening to the words of our Lord in Matthew 24:42-44? They were not watching and did not know the hour when the Lord came in judgment on Jerusalem. Their delay enabled the enemy to come and seal off the city, because they had not been listening to the words of our Lord. They were not ready in that hour when our Lord did come by way of the Romans, because He came in an hour to judge Jerusalem, when they thought not? Could it be that those who listened to our Lord had already fled the city before the Romans arrived?

After further discussion, we had prayer and the floor was open for whatever we might want to share in the time remaining. Billy did pull out of his pocket a message for Dink. He then read it out loud, as it said:

Mr. Dink---We is writin fer our Daddy whose you cheeted in the last fite, when you forrced him to fite with you! He theirfore challungas you to an other fite, which we hopes will be a fare fite withe no cheatin! It will be a fite with bear nuckles next Saturday after nune at our church at 3 oclok, and the fight will be fer six roonds or till a nockout comes. Pleas anser soon. Sinserely, Susie Belle & Liza Lou McCoy.

As I read this little note, my heart sank, not because I didn't think Dink could take care of himself, but I had been

108

praying that the Lord would break down the barrier between us and the mountain people. And now Dink would be the villain in fighting Mountain Man. And if he beat Mountain Man again, we would continue to be the villains and the enemies of the mountain people. How could this ever endear us to the hearts of these people, even if Dink lost, for we would remain, so it seemed, the enemies of this community.

Thus, it seemed that we had two options, and neither one of them was a good one. Option one was for Dink to fight Mountain Man, whereby if Dink won, we would be out of favor with the mountain people. Or Dink could lose, and we would still be the enemies of the mountain people, and Mountain Man would be their great hero. But even further, might this kind of fight get out of control, if Dink won, as some of the big mountain boys might take it upon themselves to clobber Dink and me and Billy?

Talk about a dilemma! Win and we lose! Lose and we lose! I decided I had better call Mrs. Cardieux and see how she saw things, since this was her background, though she seemed far removed from them in her life and lifestyle now. As we talked, she too was very concerned about us both. Her advice was either reply negatively to their challenge or meet their challenge and trust the Lord for the results. But she warned us, even if we replied negatively, some of the mountain boys might meet us in the dark one night and clobber us for being cowards, from their perspective. At least a fight in public would be guarded by the police---she would see to that for us.

After talking it over with Dink, we came to the conclusion that we had no other choice, except to trust the Lord and pray that God in some way would use this for His glory!

Chapter 22

As I talked these matters over further with Dink, we both acknowledged that it was difficult to deal with dishonest people. And their dishonesty was very clear, as they claimed Dink had cheated in the first fight, which was a total falsehood. We could not be dishonest this time and throw the fight, just so Mountain Man could win, because that could make things worse, as he would ride that for all it was worth. Then suddenly I saw a smile come across Dink's face, and I knew he had an idea, and when I asked him to share it with me, he laughed and said he would let me know in time---whatever that meant. So the fight was on, and I called Billy and told him the same. The fight was set up for 3:00 next Saturday afternoon at the city park. But first I would have to endure a whole week, plus the trip to the mountains, and also the teaching time, before Dink would tell me what his plan might be.

Finally, Saturday did come, and away we went early in the morning, beginning a busy day. As we flew I still couldn't get Dink to give me his plan of attack in the fight today. But he always spoke of this coming event with a smile, so I knew that it would be something special and unique. But first our study time was before us, and that was surely more interesting and important than some fight between a "Mountain Man" and a "City Slicker," which was the way they were advertising it on their cars, as I noticed as we made our way to Mrs. Cardieux's house.

First, I set before us the verses which we would be considering this day---Matthew 24:45-51---

verse 45

> Who then is a faithful and wise servant, whom his lord has made ruler over his household, to give them meat in due season?

verse 46

Blessed is that servant, who his lord when he cometh shall find him so doing!

verse 47

Verily I say unto you, That he shall make him ruler over all his goods!

verse 48

But and if that evil servant shall say in his heart, My lord delays his coming!

verse 49

And shall begin to smite his fellow servants, and to eat and drink with the drunken!

verse 50

The lord of that servant shall come in a day when he looks not for him, and in an hour that he is not aware of!

verse 51

And shall cut him asunder, and appoint his portion with the hypocrites: there shall be weeping and gnashing of teeth!

This is a general statement of the responsibility of a servant to his lord, but it is found in the context of Matthew 24 and the fall of Jerusalem, and it is applicable to that hour as well, giving us principles of a faithful and wise servant.

1. This section begins with a question! 45

    The question---

    Who then is a faithful and wise servant, whom his lord has made ruler over his household, to give them meat in due season?

2. Then comes an answer to the question! 46

The faithful servant is the one who is busy doing his Lord's will and work when He comes!

3. There will be a reward to the faithful servant! 47

The faithful servant will be put over all of his master's goods!

4. The evil servant is then clearly described! 48-51

The evil servant takes personal advantage of his lord's delay as he recognizes a selfish opportunity! 48

He begins to smite his fellow servants and he eats and drinks with the drunkards---thus a worldly and godless life-style! 49

When his lord does come, he is not waiting or expecting his lord's coming! 50

The wicked servant will be given his place with the hypocrites when his lord comes, where there will be weeping and gnashing of teeth! 51

We then discussed the fact that every Christian is a servant of the Lord's, and he or she has a clear responsibility to be faithful to their Lord, as they live upon this earth, no matter what the circumstances before us. Even if it is the reality of the fall of Jerusalem, we too have a responsibility to be faithful to our Lord.

When we had finished with a lively and healthy discussion of God's faithfulness to us and the need of our faithfulness to him, even as God's true people have been down through the ages, Dink asked a question.

"Preacha, whats we gonna do in da weeks ta come, since we seems to have finished Matthew 24."

I smiled, as I replied, "Wait and see."

I think he knew that was my comeback to his not telling me all week how he was going to fight this next battle against Mountain Man. He had let me wait all week, and now he could wait a whole week to find out where our study was going next. I did tell him that it would be related to Matthew 24 in some way.

And then the hour came, when it was time to go to the battleground, where Dink and Mountain Man would square off. As we drove to Pastor Sweet's church, Dink was very quiet, and the closer we got to the church, the greater the traffic for a mountain road. And when we got within a mile or so from the church, the traffic got even worse, and everyone had to park their car to walk to the place of the fight. It seemed like the whole state was turning out for this "big fight" between the Mountain Man and the City Slicker, as they were advertising it. I couldn't help but wonder what might erupt, if the City Slicker won.

When we finally got to the city park, which did occupy a large plot of land, there must have been several thousand people there. They had even brought in some grandstands, so all could sit and watch, and there was a regular boxing ring in the middle of it all. I began to wonder what we had gotten ourselves into?

I looked at Dink, and nothing seemed to be bothering him---no nervousness, no fear, no desire to turn back. He even had a smile on his face, as if he knew something no one else knew, and maybe he did. When the crowd saw us coming, they began to boo us, and I thought some might try to fight us, before we got to the ring. Talk about underdogs. That's what we were in their eyes.

113

Chapter 23

Soon a bell rang, and Dink pulled off his sweat clothes, and Mountain Man did the same, and as they stood in their corners, the crowd began to boo Dink. To the average man who did not know, it looked like David (Dink) going against Goliath (Mountain Man). People were laughing and sneering and making kidding statements, some of them pretty rude and crude, about Dink and his chances to win. And though there had been a stipulation of no strong drinking, I saw several with various kinds of beer, and who knows what else. Then I did see a couple of police cars parked in the mess of vehicles, but I wondered if they were there on duty or just to see the fight? There was a fellow in a referee's shirt, but he looked like a "homer" to me.

Then someone rang a bell, and Dink and "Mountain Man" met in the center of the ring and were given some final instructions. The crowd was so loud, that I couldn't hear what they were saying. And then the bell rang again, and the fight was on. Mountain Man wasted no time, as he burst out of his corner like a linebacker going after a quarterback, but Dink dodged him and Mountain Man hit his head square on the post in Dink's corner, which was holding the ropes. With Mountain Man somewhat dazed, Dink pummeled him with a right and then a left and another right and another left, which sent him spinning like a top, as he sought to get his bearings and equilibrium. But Dink gave him no room or time to recover, as he was at him again with a bevy of quick rights and lefts and rights and lefts to the face and chest and stomach, and Mountain Man hit the floor of the ring as dead weight with a thud.

I thought to myself that the Mountain Man couldn't complain that Dink had dodged him until he was exhausted in this fight. Dink had taken the fight right to him from the very beginning, and Mountain Man hadn't even touched Dink, up to this point of the fight. And then, surprisingly, someone rang the bell to end the first round, which had only lasted about 40 to 45 seconds, when each round was supposed to be three minutes. Obviously, the timer was a home-boy, also, who was trying to help Mountain Man get himself together, so he could fight another round. But they even had to help Mountain Man find his stool in his corner, so he could wake up and fight some more.

It seemed like the bell for the second round was about four or five minutes late in sounding to restart the fight, in order to give Mountain Man more time---so who's cheating now? When the bell did sound, Dink was fresh and came quickly out of his corner, but it was beginning to look rather sad, when Mountain Man could barely pull himself to his feet, and even when he did, it was obvious he was still dizzy. I told Dink before he left his corner to finish him, because the longer it went the more dangerous it was for Mountain Man's health---and for us. Dink nodded, and that is exactly what he did---he finished Mountain Man in the next 30 seconds with blows to the head and body, while Mountain Man never touched Dink, as he danced in and out, pummeling his opponent.

When Dink was finished, no referee or time keeper could do anything to prolong the fight---Mountain Man was down and out cold for the next thirty minutes, while several, maybe even some doctors, tried to revive him. The crowd then began to boo, and I wondered if they were booing Dink or Mountain Man. If they were booing Dink, it could get dangerous. Eventually the referee, if that's what one could call him, held up Dink's hand as the winner, and the crowd began to cheer him. I don't know if it was the fact that David had beaten Goliath, or that some in the crowd had some previous grudges against Mountain Man or what? Dink gave several bows, and tried to go to Mountain Man's corner, but his handlers wouldn't let him.

Instead they swept Mountain Man away, and it may have been because he was so woozy that he didn't even know who he was or where he was or what had happened. And then it seemed like every person there wanted to shake hands with Dink and pat him on the back! They were totally blown away, as to how a small man like Dink could beat up a large and powerful man like Mountain Man--- they had never seen anything like this before.

Billy came by with a big smile on his face, and then to our surprise, Mrs. Cardieux was there. She couldn't believe what she had seen either. We saw the two McCoy girls, Susie Belle and Liza Lou, but they didn't come by to say anything to us. Maybe their concern was for Mountain Man and his health, as they left with him.

There was one little girl, who came by to speak to us, who was really impressive. I guess she didn't know we were preachers, but she asked us if we were saved and knew Jesus. We assured her we did. But she wasn't satisfied with that short answer, so she sweetly asked if we had been "born again" and knew if we died right now, we would be in heaven with Jesus? When we said yes and told her we were preachers of the blessed Word of God, she lit up like a Christmas tree. I would have liked to have talked to her a little longer, but with the pressing mass of people, which wanted to greet us, I had to watch her, as she disappeared in the crowd, seeming to be by herself, for some reason. Later, I noticed from a distance, that she was still on the premises and still passing out gospel tracts.

I punched Billy and asked if he knew her, and he said no. I tried to encourage him to go over and talk to her, as she was passing out the tracts, and get to know her. Here was a young lady, who seemed to love the Lord. Could this be the girl that God had sent to him? But he was so shy, that he couldn't get up the nerve to go meet her---something he would soon regret.

Chapter 24

It took all the next week for the events of the past weekend to calm down, especially in light of those events. But a transition had been made, as far as our relationship to the mountain folks (an answer to prayer). Now, to get back to our main reason for being there---teaching Billy. We had finished Matthew 24, and were now ready to move into some other related verses and questions concerning the subject. So when the next Saturday came, and with us as rested as much as possible from the past weekend and week, we headed for the mountains once again to meet with Billy. Dink had asked me earlier what the subject was going to be, but I had not told him yet where we were going after Matthew 24.

Thus, when we met this next time, and everything had settled down, as Billy was still talking about Dink knocking out Mountain Man, I told them to turn to Matthew 25. I then announced boldly that this is the chapter which speaks of the Second Coming of Christ! I told them we would divide this chapter into several sections.

The Parable of the Ten Virgins 1-13
(The Phrase Kingdom of Heaven Immediately
Removes This Chapter from the Context
of the Fall of Jerusalem and Gives it the Context
of the Second Coming of Christ
Whereby Men Are to Be Ready for His Literal Coming!)

The kingdom of heaven is to be likened to ten virgins
    who took their lamps and went forth to meet
        the bridegroom! 1
Five of these virgins were wise and five of them were
    foolish! 2
The foolish virgins took no oil with them in their
    lamps! 3

The wise virgins took oil in their vessels with their
   lamps! 4
And while the bridegroom tarried---all the virgins
   slumbered and slept! 5
Then at midnight there came a cry---Behold the bridegroom cometh---Go ye out to meet him! 6
Thus all these virgins rose to trim their lamps---but the
   foolish virgins had no oil in their lamps and so they
      asked the wise for some oil from their lamps
         because their lamps had gone out! 7-8
But the wise answered, No---lest there be not enough oil
   for us and you both---but rather you go to those who
      sell oil and buy for yourselves! 9
But while the foolish virgins went to buy oil---the bridegroom came and they that were ready went in with him
      to the marriage and the door was shut! 10
Later the foolish virgins came, saying, Lord, Lord, open to
   us! 11
But he answered and said, Verily I say to you, I do not
   know you! 12
Watch therefore, for you know neither the day nor the hour
   wherein the Son of man cometh! 13
Analysis---

Remember our statement under the heading, which
said, "The Phrase "Kingdom of Heaven" Immediately
Removes This from the Context of the Fall of Jerusalem
and Gives It the Context of the Second Coming of Christ!"
Clearly, here the Bridegroom speaks of the Lord Jesus.
Who is coming back someday, and the virgins speak of
professing Christians, who should be ready for His Second
Coming. This will become clearer, as we move through this
chapter, noticing the different parables and their teaching.

The Parable of Three Men and Their Talents!

I Three Men Are Given Responsibilities by their lord!

The <u>kingdom of heaven</u> is again likened unto a man
who travels into a far country---but before he left
he called his servants and and separated to them
his goods for safe keeping while he was
gone! 14
To one he gave <u>five talents</u> and to another he gave <u>two</u>
<u>talents</u> and to another he gave <u>one talent</u>---and he
gave them to the men according to their several
abilities---and when he had done that he left
immediately for his journey! 15

II Three Men And What They Do with Their Talents!

The <u>first servant</u>---who was given the <u>five talents</u>---
went and traded the talents and made with them
<u>five other talents</u> profit! 16
The <u>second servant</u>---who had received <u>two talents</u>---
also gained <u>two more talents</u> with his talents! 17
The <u>third servant</u>---who had received <u>one talent</u>---went
and dug in the earth and <u>hid his lord's money</u> there
and as a result he made no gain in his
talents! 18

III Three Men Are Held Accountable for Their Talents!

   A. *A time of accountability comes when the lord
       returns---and is this not a picture of our Lord's
       return at His Second Coming?*

       Then after a long time the Lord of these servants
       came back and he reckoned with them---the three
       men---to see what they had done with his talents
       in his absence! 19

B.   The first man with five talents is held accountable!

Then <u>he that had received five talents</u> came and
brought the other five talents he had gained, and
he told his Lord he had gained five talents more!

His lord was pleased and said to him, "Well done,
thou good and faithful servant! You have been faithful over a few things and I will make you ruler over
many things---enter into the joy of thy lord!" 21

C.   The second man with two talents is accountable!

The man who had received two talents came
and said, "Lord, you gave me two talents, and I
have gained two other talents besides them!" 22

His lord was pleased and said, "Well done thou
good and faithful servant---you have been faithful
over a few things---I will make you a ruler over
many things---enter into the joy of your lord!" 23

D.   The third man with one talent is held accountable!

The man who had received one talent came
and said, Lord, I knew that you were a hard
man---reaping where you had not sown and
gathering where you had not strawed! 24

And I was afraid and went and hid your talent
in the earth---here it is and it is yours! 25

His lord answered and said to him, You wicked
and lazy servant---you knew that I reaped where

I sowed not and gathered where I have not strawed! 26

You should have put my money in the bank and then at the least at my coming I would have received my money! 27

Take therefore the talent from him and give it to him who has the ten talents! 28

For to everyone that has shall be given and he shall have an abundance---but from him that has not shall be taken away even that which he has! 29

And cast the unprofitable servant into outer darkness---where there shall be weeping and gnashing of teeth! 30

IV The Clear Statements That These Verses Speak of the Second Coming of Christ and the Reward of Believers at That Hour!

And when the Son of man shall come in His glory and all the holy angels with Him, then shall He sit upon His throne of glory! 31

And before Him shall be gathered all nations: and He shall separate them one from another, as a shepherd divides his sheep from the goats! 32

And He shall set the sheep on His right hand, but the goats on the left. 33

A. The Shepherd Rewards His True Sheep! 34-40

Then shall the king say to them on His right hand,
    Come ye blessed of my Father, and inherit the
        kingdom prepared for you from the
        foundation of the world! 34-36
    For I was hungry and you gave me meat!
    I was thirsty and you gave me drink!
    I was a stranger and you took me in!
    I was naked and you clothed me!
    I was sick and you visited me!
    I was in prison and you came to see me!
Then shall the righteous answer Him saying---37-39
    Lord, when saw we thee---
        hungry and fed You?
        thirsty and gave You drink?
        a stranger and took You in?
        naked and clothed You?
        sick or in prison and came to You?
And the King shall answer and say to you---
    Verily I say unto you---
    In as much as you have done it to one of the
        least of my brethren---you have done it
            unto Me! 40

B. *The Shepherd Judges the False Sheep! 41-43*

Then shall He say to them on the left hand---
    Depart from me, ye cursed, into everlasting
        fire which is prepared for the devil and his
            angels! 41
I was hungry and you gave me no food! 42
I was thirsty and you gave me no drink! 42
I was a stranger and you did not take me in! 43
I was naked and you did not clothe me! 43
I was sick and in prison and you did not visit me! 43

Then shall they answer Him saying---44
    Lord, when did we see you when you were
        hungry   or thirsty
        or a stranger   or naked
        or sick   or in prison
        and we did not minister to you?
Then shall He answer them saying---45
    Verily I say unto you that in as much as you
        did it not to one of the least of these---
            you did it not unto me!
And these shall go into everlasting punishment---
    but the righteous into eternal life! 46

CONCLUSION

1. Thus Matthew 25 clearly speaks of the Second Coming
   of Christ!

   in the parable of the Bridegroom Coming---
       there is the phrase "the kingdom of heaven!
       there is the clarity of people waiting for the coming
           of the Bridegroom---the Lord Jesus Christ!
       there is the reality of one group of people who are
           ready to be received by the Bridegroom when
           He comes!
       there is the reality of another group of people who
           are unprepared when He comes and they are not
           taken when He comes!
       there is a warning that we are to watch for we know
           not the day or the hour when the Son of man
           comes!
   in the parable of the talents!
       all will be held accountable when the Lord
           comes!

the text clearly states that the Son of Man is coming
in all His glory to sit upon His throne of glory!
all nations shall come before Him and He will
separate the His sheep from the goats!
His sheep will be placed on His right hand and the
goats will be placed on His left hand!
Christ will reward His true sheep and He will tell
His false sheep to depart from Him into everlasting fire which is prepared for the devil
and his angels---for they are cursed!
the final statement is very clear---
the wicked will go into everlasting punishment
but the righteous will go into eternal life!

When we had finished our study, Billy wanted to know if he could ask a question, even though it was not a Biblical question? I told him to go ahead, but no answers could be guaranteed in light of such a broad possibility of the question. His question was, did we know yet who the young lady was who was passing out the gospel tracts at the fight the other day? Dink and I both shook our heads indicating a negative to his question. Plus, I reminded him he should have introduced himself to her, as I suggested.

He then admitted that he had been thinking about her and praying for her ever since that day, and he said he thought he had seen her in one of his services somewhere previously. But he had preached in so many churches, he couldn't possibly place her in the right church, even as he had racked his brain to remember.

I told him that if it was God's will, he would meet her again some day, some way, in some place, all according to God's will and plan and purpose. Till then keep praying for His will to be done in the matter, whatever that might be.

Chapter 25

There was no further word or update on the mountain situation, so when the next Saturday came, and with us as rested as possible from the past weekends and weeks, we were off to the mountains once again to meet with Billy. We had already shown from Matthew 25 the reality of the Second Coming of Christ, in contrast to Matthew 24, which spoke of the Fall of Jerusalem. Today we were going to deal with Acts 1:10-11, looking for other clear passages concerning the Second Coming of Christ, since some believed that Matthew 24 spoke of the Fall of Jerusalem and that was the hour of His Second Coming.

And while they looked steadfastly toward heaven as He went up, behold, two men stood by them in white apparel, who also said, Ye men of Galilee, why stand ye gazing up into heaven? This same Jesus, who is taken up from you into heaven, <u>shall so come in like manner,</u> as ye have seen Him go into heaven!

I paused a moment to let these verses sink in, and I would suggest the reader do the same just now as well. I continued, that whether one realizes it or not, some do believe that the Second Coming of Christ was fulfilled in Matthew 24, when Jerusalem fell, which means our Lord has already come and that He is not literally coming in the future. That is to say again, some believe the Second Coming of Christ has already taken place, and many of these say it was at the time of the judgment of Jerusalem in 70 AD as seen in Matthew 24.

But could it be that Matthew 24 speaks of the fall of Jerusalem, while other verses in the New Testament speak of a literal Second Coming of Christ to this earth, and this was the reason we studied Matthew 25, and also why I had just now quoted Acts 1:10-11?

We have already noted that there are many "comings" of the Lord in the Bible, which are not literal, for many times He comes to judge men. But there are other verses which teach clearly that Christ is coming back literally in bodily form in the Second Coming. A person, therefore, is wrong to say that all words, which are used of our Lord's coming are symbolic, and it is equally wrong to say that all words which speak of our Lord's coming are literal. We have already seen in Matthew 25 one of the clearest of the passages which teach the Lord's literal and bodily Second Coming, and now we will see the same in Acts 1:10-11. This is the passage which says the following---that Christ was taken from this earth, going up into heaven, and as His followers were watching Him go up into heaven, and as they looked steadfastly towards heaven, two men stood by them in white apparel and said:

You men of Galilee!

Why stand you gazing into heaven?

This <u>same Jesus</u> who is taken up from you into heaven
    shall so come **in like manner** <u>as you have seen Him
    go into heaven</u>!

The key phrase here is "<u>shall so come in like manner as you have seen Him go into heaven</u>," and the question is what does the Bible mean when it says He will come back "in like manner?" Literally, it means Christ will come back in the same manner and in the same mode or way as they had seen Him going away into heaven in the first chapter of Acts. Which is to say that Jesus was taken up into heaven bodily, and His followers, who watched Him go up as He left them, saw His bodily exit from this earth, and the promise is that He will come back in like manner or in the same manner---bodily---just as they saw Him go into heaven! Don't miss the key statements of these two verses. "Like manner" speaks of a bodily return. Here is a summary of these verses---

Jesus went up into heaven bodily!
He was seen going up into heaven bodily!
The same Jesus will come back again bodily!
Thus, there will be a bodily Second Coming of Christ!
And this did not take place at the hour of the fall of
  Jerusalem---He did not come back then bodily!
Therefore we must conclude that His bodily return
  to this earth is yet to take place!

And this will continue to be the purpose of the second portion of our study, that just as Matthew 25 speaks of the Second Coming of Christ bodily in the future, Acts 1:10-11 and other verses teach the same thing. Therefore, I would ask anyone, who is reading this book thus far, not to put all of those who believe that Matthew 24 speaks of the Fall of Jerusalem in any category, which denies the literal Second Coming of Christ in bodily form, because that IS NOT the viewpoint or position of all who would see Matthew 24 as the Fall of Jerusalem. Which is to say again that we do have firm convictions that Matthew 24 speaks of the fall of Jerusalem. But we would also possess very firm convictions that the literal and bodily return of Christ, according to other passages of Scripture, is yet to take place---He will so return in like manner as He went away.
  Thus we must conclude---
    Jesus will come back to this earth in the future!
    Jesus will come back to this earth bodily!
    Jesus will come back to this earth in great power!
    Jesus will come back to this earth in great glory!
    Jesus will come back for the saved of all ages!
    Jesus will come back to take us home to heaven!
    And so shall we then ever be with the Lord!
  None of this can take place without His coming---a literal coming as these and other verses indicate. Acts 1:10-11 is very clear on a future literal second coming of Christ.

Chapter 26

As we traveled home that Saturday evening, I kept trying to think of some way we could help Billy find the young lady who was passing out tracts at the fight between Dink and Mountain Man. And also my mind was on Mountain Man himself, as well, wondering how he was doing since the fight. Could I call him or go see him somehow, maybe seeking to build some bridges between him and us, or would all our efforts be rebuffed in light of the beatings he had taken twice from Dink. It was rather ironic now that Billy was not being bothered by those he didn't want to see, and the young lady he really wanted to meet was nowhere to be found.

I couldn't help but wonder, if the Lord was teaching us something, and that was that there may be times when the Lord gives us what we don't want (in this case an opportunity to witness to some old hard-headed knucklehead like Mountain Man), while at the same time He keeps us from getting what we do want from Him (in this case, again, to be able to find the young lady Billy so wanted to meet).

The week passed quickly, and then it was on the Friday night, just before we left on Saturday, that I got a phone call from Billy. He said Mountain Man wanted to see us (Dink and me), while we were in town this coming weekend. I asked him if he knew what he wanted to see us about, and he said no---just that he wanted to see us. He said Mountain Man still sounded like he was hurting from the fight, but he was as gracious and humble as Billy had ever seen him. I told Billy that this is the way some people act, when they want to get even with you for something, or it really could be a legitimate humbling from God. I told Billy to set up a meeting with him for just after our study, and we would see him before we took off for home.

But then, I hadn't been off the phone for five minutes, when it rang again, and a soft female voice responded to my "Hello!" She wanted to know if this was Dr. Ira Pointer, who had been teaching a Billy Hill in the mountain area, and the one who had a side-kick named Dink? I could tell she was from the mountains by her brogue, but I must admit I wondered if it was Susie Belle or Liza Lou or maybe even the tract girl!

I assured her immediately that I was Dr. Ira Pointer, and that I had been teaching Billy Hill, and then I asked her who she was and what I could do for her, and though I didn't tell her this---my first guess would have been that she was the tract girl. She didn't identify herself, but she said she wanted to thank me for teaching Billy, as I had been doing. I responded by asking if she knew Billy, and she answered, "Yes!" When I asked how she knew Billy, she would not give me that information, but she simply said that years ago she had a crush on Billy, but he didn't even know she was alive!

I tried to tell her that's the way young boys are. They don't wake up to the young ladies around them, usually, till sometimes after the girls have awakened to them, especially a shy boy like Billy. Then I asked her if she knew Billy, and she answered, "Yes!" When I asked how and when she had met him, she chuckled and said, "Quite awhile ago. He probably doesn't even remember me now."

Then I just had to get brave and ask her, "Are you the young lady, who was passing out tracts on the Saturday at the fight?"

And with that she said, "I have to go now! Thanks!" and she hung up on me. I thought to myself, as I sat down in my easy chair to think, "In His time!" God is working and in His time, who knows what He might bring to pass concerning this godly young lady and Billy.

Chapter 27

We heard nothing further from the mountain area, but soon we were on our way back to the mountains to take care of several matters. Of course, there was our study, but we would also meet with Mountain Man at his request, which wouldn't leave much time for anything else. Flying up Saturday morning early and then home in the afternoon was a long enough day without crowding something else in, but this seemed to have become our pattern on Saturdays.

As we met with Billy, before we began our study, I asked him if there was anything new, and he said not to his knowledge, so I concluded there had been no more word from the gospel tract girl. And after prayer, our study began.

Noting New Testament Verses Which Speak
of the Second coming of Christ!
ACTS

I told them this would be our pursuit for the rest of our study, because there were some people, as we had already noted, who having shown correctly that Matthew 24 speaks of the fall of Jerusalem because of its context, they then say also that the fall of Jerusalem included the hour of the Second Coming of our Lord, which means the Second Coming has already taken place. Thus, it is clear that these deny a literal and bodily return of Christ to this earth in the future. We had already seen that Matthew 24 was the fall of Jerusalem, but it was not the Second Coming of Christ, but Matthew 25 did speak of the Second Coming of our Lord.

Now it was our desire to look at other places in the New Testament, as we had done with Acts 1:10-11 to show that was the case also, that is, that the Second Coming of Christ is yet to take place. We would now see if there were other books of the New Testament, which spoke of the Second

Coming. We would move through all the other New Testament books besides the gospels, to see if these other New Testament books had recorded the future event of our Lord's bodily return to this earth---His Second Coming.

As just noted, we had already seen that Acts spoke clearly of Christ's personal bodily return to earth in 1:10-11, as it said, *10 And while they looked steadfastly toward heaven as he went up, behold, two men stood by them in white apparel; 11 Which also said, Ye men of Galilee, why stand ye gazing up into heaven? this same Jesus, which is taken up from you into heaven, shall so come in like manner as ye have seen him go into heaven.* But surprisingly that seemed to be the only place in Acts where the Second Coming is mentioned. I told them further, that they might very well be surprised at the number of passages which do speak of the Second Coming--not as many as one might imagine. And we did admit it might be possible that we could miss some in one of the New Testament books.

This is not to argue against the Second Coming of Christ in the future, because if just one verse in the Bible mentioned His Second Coming, we would be bound to believe the truth of the doctrine of His bodily return to this earth. It is true in some cases that other of the New Testament books have very little to say concerning His bodily return to this earth, something which may surprise us, since so many have spent so much time preaching on this subject. Not that preaching on that subject of the Second Coming is wrong, but some preach on this subject so often, as if it were the major subject of the New Testament. So, believe it or not, the book of Acts is not a major book on the Second Coming of Christ, but the one verse, Acts 1:10-11. is a very enlightening and powerful verse.

ROMANS

I told them next that I was further surprised, when I checked Romans on the subject of the Second Coming of our Lord. Romans 8:23 speaks of the redemption of the body, but it says no more than that, which is to say that this area of truth in Paul's discussion is not clearly related to the Second Coming. Again, we warn, do not take this as a negative statement, but only as a recognition of the reality that some Biblical books do not give the Second Coming of Christ the place some modern preachers do---the supreme place in their preaching.

I CORINTHIANS

I must say again that the next book in the New Testament, the book of I Corinthians, surprised me in the other direction---the number of times it mentions the Second Coming. Following are the verses I found which said something about this subject. We didn't have much discussion over any of them, but a few words on some, because some were quite obvious and needed little discussion.

I Corinthians 4:5

Judge nothing before the time the Lord comes!

I Corinthians 5:5

This verse speaks of the spirit being saved (a man's spirit) in the day of the Lord, which is often noted as a reference to Christ's Second Coming, but not as clearly as some others!

I Corinthians 11:26

This verse reads, *26 For as often as you eat this bread and drink this cup, you proclaim the Lord's death till He comes.* One wonders how one can deny this as a verse which speaks of Christ's Second Coming?

I Corinthians 15:23

This verse reads, *23 But every man in his own order: Christ the firstfruits; afterward they that are Christ's at his coming.* This speaks of Christ being the first fruits of the resurrection, as He rose first in order of time. Then comes the resurrection of those who are Christ's, not immediately after His resurrection, but even centuries later, as we can see from our perspective. The text clearly states that the resurrection of the saints is late in history <u>at the hour of Christ's coming</u>!

I Corinthians 15:52

This verse reads, *In a moment, in the twinkling of an eye, at the last trump: for the trumpet shall sound, and the dead shall be raised incorruptible, and we shall be changed.* This is a Second Coming text because it speaks of the dead in Christ being raised at the last trump, which is associated with His Second Coming.

Summary of these verses---
1. Judge nothing till the Lord comes!
2. The Lord's Supper shows His death till He comes!
3. We are the part of His fruits at His coming!
4. At the last trump the dead are raised---a clear statement of our Lord's Second Coming!

Summary of other points we had made---
1. Acts has one verse which speaks of the SC!
2. Romans has no clear verses which speak of the SC!
3. I Corinthians has five verses which clearly speak of the SC!

As we closed and gathered our things, I asked Billy where we were supposed to meet Mountain Man, and Billy said we would meet him at Mountain Man's church. I asked if his preacher, Pastor Sweet, would be there, and he said he didn't know. And so we left for our rendezvous with great uncertainty!

Chapter 28

It didn't take us long, when we met with Mountain Man and Pastor Sweet, to learn that they both had made a profession of faith in Christ, and their attitudes seemed to evidence something, or else they were pretty good actors. After Dink and I had a good talk with them, and they both gave a seemingly credible profession of faith in Christ, we prayed rejoicing in their salvation, and we sat a few moments talking to them further of what it is to be a true Christian. I must say, all the bluster and arrogance was gone, out of Mountain Man, so it seemed, and he even asked us to call him Brother Roy from now on, as that was his name. Pastor Sweet also gave a strong confession of salvation, as he had been influenced by the salvation of Brother Roy (I almost said Mountain Man here). They said they had been studying the Bible together, and Roy had led his wife to the Lord, also, but the girls were skeptical of his profession of faith. With a smile he said quietly, "The Lord is gonna convince them girls too that Jesus is real!"

And then they just couldn't thank us enough for witnessing to them, though our witness was more by our actions than by our words. Or maybe it was just our demeanor and seriousness about the things of God, and maybe even that we were not afraid of him, and trusted the Lord, as he had blustered against us. And maybe he even thought that Dink beating him up in two fights was by the power of God, as he realized that if the Lord was with us, how could he stand against us. Whatever had happened and why it happened, was of God, and we spent several hours rejoicing together and suggesting books for them to read, as they grew in the Christian life.

With tears and deep thanks and love and sympathy to each other, we all parted, as Dink and I knew we had to get on home---we were already hours late. When finally in the air, I smiled and began to laugh, and Dink wondered what I was laughing about. When I finally contained my laughter, I set before him my humor, as I asked him if he realized we had practiced in the past few weeks a new kind of evangelism? Fist-fight Evangelism---winning a man to Christ by having two fights with him, as we beat the tar out of him! This surely must be a unique and different kind of a way to reach men for the Lord, I said jokingly. I told Dink that, honestly, I preferred the old way---showing men the truth of the gospel in our witnessing. But maybe some are so hard-hearted and hard-headed that the Lord could use even this unique means to reach men---Fist-Fight Evangelism---but only if they start the fight. I was only kidding, but Dink, the purest in evangelistic practices, frowned at me, as he told me the church had enough false ways to do evangelism without our adding a new heretical one to the list.

It wasn't long before we both were dozing as we shot through the sky. And then, believe it or not, I thought the engine began to sputter again, which made me wonder if that was the work of men against us once more, or if it was just the airplane itself having problems without the help of men, which cars and airplanes can do. Then I woke up, and discovered I had been dreaming in my sleep. I guess my mind had sub-consciously gotten use to the engines sputtering, and my thoughts had been played out in my dreams, as we traveled through the air.

To be honest, as much as I had enjoyed these mountain experiences, I was ready for them to end. Hopefully, just a few more weeks and it would all be over. But we would never forget the mountain folks and Billy and his problems.

.

Chapter 29

I had already learned that weekends can be the fastest days of the week, but it seems the weekends since we began going to the mountains had gotten faster and faster with the passing of each month. Plus, weekends usually consisted of even now of driving somewhere to preach on a Sunday, and many times it was an all day excursion, as I preached in the morning and in the evening, returning home twice as exhausted as I was, when I had gotten home on Saturday from my trip to the mountain area.

My wife kiddingly told me that I was getting too old for such youthful excursions, and I think I almost agreed with her. I promised her and encouraged myself by telling her that we would only be a few more weekends traveling to the mountains, and then she asked me how I defined "few" and I smiled and never gave her an answer. And, yes, the next Saturday trip to the mountains came too soon for me, and probably for her as well, as we parted once again on the next Saturday and were soon at our destination of study.

I reminded them that, having completed our study of Matthew 24, which had spoken of the fall of Jerusalem in light of the context of that chapter, that we were now seeking to understand what the rest of the New Testament said about the Second Coming of Christ. We were looking to see if the New Testament did in other places speak clearly of the Second Coming of Christ in the future. We had already looked at Matthew 25, and the book of Acts, and also Romans and I Corinthians, concerning the Second Coming, and we had found some clear references which could not be denied---they were definitely speaking about Christ coming back to this earth again bodily some day in the future. Which meant that those who do not see a future Second Coming of Christ, but who thought He came again at the time of the fall of Jerusalem are incorrect in their thinking.

We were now ready to move on to the next book of the Bible and and see what it said about the Second Coming of Christ.

II CORINTHIANS

The fact of the matter is that II Corinthians has no clear reference to the Second Coming of Christ, that we could find. It does refer to "the day of the Lord Jesus," and many think that in some way refers to the Second Coming. But we were looking for very clear statements concerning this great event of the future! II Corinthians 1:14 says, *As also ye have acknowledged us in part, that we are your rejoicing, even as ye also are ours in <u>the day of the Lord Jesus</u>.*

Again, this is not to say that this passage does not speak of the Second Coming, but in light of our specific pursuit to deal with some who deny a future Second Coming of Christ altogether, we were looking for verses which are very clear concerning this great event. Thus, we had to conclude that II Corinthians had no clear and definite verses that we could find, which spoke of the Second Coming of Christ.

GALATIANS

There are no specific references to the Second Coming of Christ in Galatians that we found.

EPHESIANS

Again, there are no specific references in the book of Ephesians to the Second Coming of Christ. Ephesians 4:30 does have a reference to the day of redemption, as it says, *And do not grieve the Holy Spirit of God, by whom you were sealed unto <u>the day of redemption</u>.* The mentioning here of the "day of redemption" is seen by many as the hour of our Lord's Second Coming. But again this is not a specific certain reference to the Second Coming of Christ, that is, a reference which would be the clear evidence, whereby we could seek to convince those who teach that the Second Coming has already taken place.

PHILIPPIANS

Again, I had to say that there are no clear references to the Second Coming of Christ in the book of Philippians. However, again there are references which many might use to speak of the Second Coming, such as 2:16, which speaks of "the day of Christ," and 3:21, which says "Christ will change our bodies," and again 4;5, which says, "The Lord is at hand." But again, these are not in a context which specifically speaks of the Second Coming of Christ, though again some see them as such references to that hour of His coming. And with this I have no problem, but others might want verses on the Second Coming to be absolutely specific and clear.

COLOSSIANS

Again, we must note that the Second Coming of Christ is not found in Colossians in any clear and exact reference. There is the phrase that "we shall appear with Him in glory" in 3:4, but again that is not an absolutely clear and undeniable reference to the Second Coming of Christ.

I THESSALONIANS

Again, there are several verses which seem to speak of the Second Coming in I Thessalonians . We will take them one by one and let the reader be the judge:

I Thessalonians 1:10

Paul speaks of how the Thessalonians turned from idols to serve the living God and <u>to wait for His Son from heaven</u>, whom God raised from the dead, even Jesus, who delivers us from the wrath to come. Some might argue that this too speaks of the hour of the fall of Jerusalem, but it seems to speak clearly of a resurrection hour, which will deliver us from the wrath of God to come, which does seem to be the final wrath to come upon this world at the Second Coming of Christ---we will be rescued from it. So this would be a clear statement of His Second Coming!

I Thessalonians 4:13-17

Several truths are here in these verses and they also seem to speak of the Second Coming of Christ!

1. Paul says he does not want them to be ignorant! 13
2. Paul does not want them to be ignorant of those who have died---that is, those who have fallen asleep in Christ! 13
3. Paul does not want them to sorrow for those loved one as if they have no hope! 13
4. Paul tells them that if they believe Jesus died and rose again, even so, those who are asleep in Jesus---that is those who have died---God will bring with Him---this clearly seems to speak of the Second Coming of Christ---He will raise these dead saints who have died and He will bring those with Him when He comes back again!
5. Paul then states very clearly the following--- he speaks by the Word of the Lord! he says we who are alive and remain unto the coming of the Lord shall not prevent

those who are asleep in the Lord (that is those who have died)---from coming back with Christ when He comes again! 15

6. Paul says the Lord Himself shall descend from heaven---which certainly is speaking of His Second Coming--and He will come with a shout and with the voice of the archangel and with the trump of God! 16

7. Paul says the dead in Christ shall rise first and then we who are alive and remain on earth shall be caught up together to meet the Lord in the air, and so we shall ever be with the Lord! This verse also clearly speaks of the Second Coming of Christ!

I Thessalonians 5:1-10

Paul again seems clearly to speak of the Second Coming of Christ in the following verses!

1. Paul tells his readers they already know of the times and the seasons! 1

2. Paul says they know perfectly that the day of the Lord comes as a thief in the night (which seems to be speaking of the Second Coming of Christ)! 2

3. Paul says when men say, "Peace and safety!" it is then that sudden destruction comes upon them as travail upon a woman---and they shall not escape! 3

4. Paul says the Thessalonians are not in the darkness that this day should overtake them as a thief! 4

5. Paul says they are all the children of light and the children of day and not the children of the darkness! 4

6. Paul instructs them not to sleep---as do others---but watch and be sober (and ready)---because it is the sleepers who sleep at night and the drunkards who are drunk at night! 6-7

7. Paul says again that those of us who are of the day must be sober putting on the breastplate of faith and love, and a helmet---the hope of salvation! 8

8. Paul says God has not appointed us to wrath but to salvation by our Lord Jesus Christ. And this seems to be the strongest evidence that he is speaking of the Second Coming, because that hour has no wrath for us, but joy as we meet our Lord in the air, as we are delivered from the final wrath, which will fall upon this earth! 9

9. Paul says it matters not how we meet the Lord--- being one who is sleeping when He comes (has died) or whether we are awake (living) at His coming---we shall be with Him in that hour! 10

Thus we have to say again that some books of the New Testament do speak clearly of the Second Coming of Christ, while some have verses which might be speaking of the Second Coming, and there are other books of the New Testament, that do not mention the Second Coming of Christ. We have not covered all the New Testament books, but such is true of the ones looked at up to this point of our study.

We spent the rest of our time discussing other matters, and we took advantage of this opportunity to ask Billy about Brother Roy and Pastor Sweet. He said he had not seen either one of them, but he had heard something---that they were "running" a meeting, and there was a real moving of the Spirit at these services.

Chapter 30

As we returned home, my mind was busy working on a new tract, one which might gain the attention of "the tract girl!" This was the first tract I had ever written, but it must have been of the Lord, because I had finished it (in my mind) by the time we arrived home, And by the middle of the next week, I had it at the printer, so we could take it with us the next Saturday. I discussed the matter with Mrs. Cardieux, and she said we could even offer it free to those who wanted to distribute it, which would give it a greater distribution. Thus, that next week Mrs. Cardieux ran an ad in the local paper, offering it to churches and individuals free. After that, it was wait and see what came to us in the way of orders, which then would require us to see if we could figure out if any orders were from the tract girl.

Thus, we were killing two birds with one stone! The greater bird would be that we were getting out the gospel, and the secondary bird was the finding of the young lady we had named "the tract girl." I could hardly wait for the orders to come in, and we would leave the identity of the young lady to the Lord, just as we would leave the distribution of the tracts to the Lord's people, also, so men could get the plan of salvation. But the greater priority to all of this was our hour of study concerning the Second Coming of Christ in the New Testament. So after arriving at our destination, we turned to the book of II Thessalonians to see if there were any clear references to the Second Coming of Christ in that New Testament book.

II THESSALONIANS 1:7-9

7 And to you who are troubled, rest with us, when the Lord Jesus shall be revealed from heaven with His mighty angels. 8 In flaming fire taking vengeance on them that know not God, and obey not the gospel of our

Lord Jesus Christ. 9 Who shall be punished with everlasting destruction from the presence of the Lord and from the glory of His power, 10 <u>When He shall come</u> to be glorified in His saints, and to be admired in all them that believe (because our testimony among you was believed) in that day. A summary follows---

1. Some day the Lord Jesus is going to be revealed from heaven with His mighty angels! 7

2. In that day <u>He will come</u> with His angels in flaming fire to take vengeance on them that know not God and obey not the gospel of the Lord Jesus Christ (surely this speaks of the Second Coming of Christ!) 8

3. These will be punished with everlasting destruction from the presence of the Lord and from the glory of His power! 9

4. This is the hour <u>He shall come</u> to be glorified in His saints and to be admired in all them that believe! 10

Which is to say, that the Second Coming of Christ will be a time, when He comes in flaming fire to take vengeance on the lost, as they will be punished with everlasting destruction; and it is the hour also when He comes to be glorified in His saints and to be admired in all them that believe on Him! This passage surely speaks of the Second Coming of our Lord Jesus Christ!

II THESSALONIANS 2:1-17

(This is a long passage but your author thinks we must see it as a whole to understand it clearly as the Second Coming of our Lord).

1 Now we beseech you, brethren, by the <u>coming</u> of our

Lord Jesus Christ, and by <u>our gathering together unto</u> <u>Him,</u> 2 That ye be not soon shaken in mind, or be troubled, neither by spirit, nor by word, nor by letter as from us, as the <u>day of the Christ</u> (the Lord) is present. 3 Let no man deceive you by any means; for that day shall not come except there come a (the) falling away first, and that man of sin be revealed, the son of perdition, 4 Who opposeth and exalteth himself above all that is called God, or that is worshiped, so that he, as God sitteth in the temple of God, showing himself that he is God. 5 Remember ye not that, when I was yet with you, I told you these things? 6 And now ye know what withholdeth (restrains) that he might be revealed in his time. 7 For the mystery of iniquity doth already work; only he who now letteth will let (will continue to hinder) until he be taken out of the way. 8 And then shall that wicked one be revealed, whom the Lord shall consume with the spirit of His mouth, and <u>shall destroy</u> <u>with the brightness of His coming,</u> 9 Even him whose coming is after the working of Satan with all power and signs & lying wonders, 10 And with all deceivableness of unrighteousness in them that perish, because they received not the love of the truth, that they might be saved. 11 And for this cause God shall send them strong delusions, that they should believe a (the) lie, 12 That they all might be damned who believed not the truth, but had pleasure in unrighteousness.

1. Paul says he is addressing them in a strong manner in light of the <u>coming of the Lord</u> <u>Jesus Christ,</u> and by the fact that this will be <u>the hour of our gathering together unto</u> <u>Christ!</u> 1

2. Paul wants them not to be soon shaken in their minds or troubled neither by spirit or by

word or by a letter from him, to the effect
the day of the Lord has already come.
(which is to say that the day of the Lord or
the Second Coming has not yet come!) 2

3. Paul warns them not to allow any man to deceive them---because the day of the Lord
shall not come except there comes first the
apostasy or falling away, when the son of
perdition will be revealed! 3

4. Paul warns again that the son of perdition
opposes and exalts himself above all that is
called God or that is worshiped so that he
as God sits in the temple of God, showing
himself that he is God! 4

5. Paul then reminds them that he warned them of
such things when he was with them! 5

6. Paul reminds them that now they know what
restrains this one he has mentioned---the one
who opposes and exalts himself above all
that is God---he will be revealed in God's
time---when his hour comes! 6

7. Paul states clearly that the mystery of iniquity
(this wicked one who is coming) does
already work, but there is one who now
hinders this wicked one and he will continue
to hinder this wicked one until the one
hindering is taken out of the way! 7

8. Paul says then that wicked one shall be
revealed and the Lord will consume that
wicked one with the spirit of His mouth
and the Lord shall destroy him with the
brightness of His coming! 8

9. Paul says this wicked one, who is coming, is the
one working by the power of Satan and he

145

works with all the power and signs and lying
wonders of Satan! 9

10. Paul says further that this one works with all the
deceivableness of unrighteousness in those
who perish, for they received not the love of
the truth, that they might be saved! 10

11. Paul states clearly that for this cause God shall
send them strong delusion, that they should
believe a (the) lie, that they all might be
damned who believed not the truth, but
had pleasure in unrighteousness. 11-12

Some authors have said that this passage of Scripture in
II Thessalonians 2:1-17 could be either the Fall of
Jerusalem or the Second Coming of Christ. I would beg
to differ with that viewpoint and would see this section
speaking of the Second Coming for the following
reasons.

1. Paul calls this the coming of the Lord Jesus Christ
and the hour of our gathering together unto Christ!
The destruction of Jerusalem was never seen as a
gathering of God's people unto Himself, but always
as a period of judgment! (verse 1)

2. There have been times of falling away prior to the
Fall of Jerusalem, but such was the Jewish race all
throughout the Old Testament days and into the
New Testament days prior to the death of Christ.
Plus, a man of sin is spoken of here, one who would
be revealed, and though there was much sin in the
days of Christ and following, there was no man of
sin as wicked as the one prophesied here in that he
is even called the son of perdition and in that he

opposes and exalts himself above all that is called God and even demands to be worshiped! 3-4

3. Plus, there is no seeming evidence that the hinderer, which seems to be a reference to the Holy Spirit, has been taken out of the way, neither in the New Testament period nor in the long history of the church nor in our day. 7-8

4. Thus, the conclusion must be that the context of our passage and what is described in this passage better fits the Second Coming of Christ than the Fall of Jerusalem.

II THESSALONIANS 3:5

And the Lord direct your hearts into the love of God, and into the patient waiting for Christ.

1. This is a brief verse and not absolutely clear that it is or isn't speaking of the Second Coming of Christ. But in light of the other verses we have seen in II Thessalonians, it may be speaking of His Second Coming, as the verse does challenge us to direct our hearts into a patient waiting for Christ---waiting for Christ to come again.

Following some further discussion, we called it a day. But then Billy smiled, as he told us that he had seen her today. He had even followed her home without her seeing him. It seems her father is some official, not in his town, but in the next town over.

Chapter 31

I asked Billy if he had gone to her door and knocked, so he could make her acquaintance, and he said, "No!" I asked him if he had seen a name on the mail box, so he would know here name, and he said, "No!" I asked him if he knew anyone else in that neighborhood, who could give him her name or phone number, and he said, "No!" I asked him if he had a plan to meet her in the future, and he said, "No!"

It seemed like he was mystified at this hour, just because he had found out where she lived, and he didn't know what to do about it or didn't want to do anything about it, except to fantasize in his mind about her, being too shy to face her. That is understandable, because the girls he had dated previously were too forward and pressed a relationship with him, because they had an ulterior motive. But this young lady was real. and she had no false motive, but her desire was to serve the Lord first, and other things came in second in her life. Surely this attitude and demeanor was evidence of a godly girl, who put the Lord first, and I told Billy that, and all he could do was smile, as he seemed to be enjoying just thinking about her now. He had no plan whereby he could meet her.

By this time, Mrs. Cardieux had joined us, and as she had listened to the conversation, she concluded this girl's father was a local city judge of the next town, a Judge Jameson, who had a strong Christian testimony himself. As I looked at Billy, the smile was gone from his face, and when I asked him why the smile was gone, he said he didn't know whether he wanted to date a judge's daughter or not. Why couldn't her father be just a good old mountain boy?

I asked him if he had ever been invited to preach at their church, and he said not that he could remember. But then he added that he was quite young when he began to preach, and maybe he couldn't remember, or maybe even they didn't live in that town then. But a smile then came to his face again, as he said, "At least I know who she is now and where she lives."

Then Mrs. Cardiuex thoughtfully added, "I think I know that girl. I had almost forgotten, but I met a young lady in her very town, when I was there on business, at which time I spoke of the Lord, and it was so obvious that she knew the Lord and loved the Lord and put the Lord first in her life. And, yes, as I remember, she knew her Bible and doctrine. I even wondered where she had learned so much about Scripture and the truth of the Word of God."

And then she added something that sort of took the wind out of Billy's sails, when she said, "She told me she thought the Lord was calling her to be a missionary, like Lottie Moon or Amy Carmichael or Ann Judson. And she said that might rule out her ever getting married in light of the fact that neither Lottie Moon nor Amy Carmichael ever got married. But then I reminded her that Ann Judson had married Adoniram Judson, and she had died at a very young age.

I could tell by the look on Billy's face that such words discouraged him in that he was not called to be a missionary---he was called to preach to these mountain folks, which meant she might not be the girl for him to marry some day. Then I told him that all of this was in God's hands, and he must be willing to submit to God, whatever His will might be. And then I told him, that often when people read about the lives of the great missionaries, which is what she seems to have been doing, that one has a burden for a lost world, and even thinks they might be called to be a missionary, and that is good, in that all believers need to have a burden for missions. But that does not mean that we all are called to go to the mission field.

His countenance changed as he said "At least I know who she is, and God knows His will for both of us, and that is all that matters!"

Chapter 32

All the way home I couldn't get over the statement that "the tract girl" wanted to be a missionary like Lottie Moon or Amy Carmichael or Ann Judson---three of the greatest missionaries of history, and, yes, probably THE three greatest women missionaries of history, also. It seemed clear that Billy had never even heard of these three dear ladies or read one of their lives. I shared that with Dink, and he too stated his surprise, wondering how a mountain girl had learned so much about truth and witnessing and missionaries---she had to be one in a million. I don't say that to put down the mountain folk, for most city folk who are believers, are just as ignorant concerning the matter of missions. But I say it to recognize an unusual young lady, who was, maybe, even miles ahead of Billy and his knowledge of the truth, even though he was a preacher boy. I almost didn't even know how to pray for Billy now, concerning a young lady friend, except God's will be done?

And yes, before long we were headed back to the mountains, and soon we were into our study once again. This day's study seemed rather easy, because most of the Biblical chapters we looked at had no references to the Second Coming, so I set forth that information as follows.

I TIMOTHY

I Timothy 1---No references to the Second Coming!
I Timothy 2---No references to the Second Coming!
I Timothy 3---No references to the Second Coming!
I Timothy 4---No references to the Second Coming!
I Timothy 5---No references to the Second Coming!
I Timothy 6:13-14

> This is the only reference in I Timothy to the SC. Paul has just given Timothy several commands, but now he seems to be speaking of his final command of this section, as he states, "I command thee in the

sight of God, Who quickeneth all things (maketh all things alive), and before Christ Jesus, Who before Pontius Pilate witnessed a good confession, that you keep this commandment without spot, unrebukable until the appearing of our Lord Jesus Christ!

The command which they are to keep in such a very serious manner until the appearing of Christ is that they are to fight the good fight of faith, and lay hold on eternal life, unto which they have been called, and which they have already professed a good profession before many witnesses.

II TIMOTHY

II Timothy 1---No references to the Second Coming!
II Timothy 2---No references to the Second Coming!
II Timothy 3---No references to the Second Coming!
II Timothy 4:1
   Paul speaks of Christ judging the quick and the dead at His appearing and His kingdom---which seems to be a reference to His Second Coming!
II Timothy 4:8---Paul speaks of the crown of righteousness that the Lord shall give him in that day, not to him only, but to all those who love His appearing--- the phrase "His appearing" again seems to speak of the Second Coming of Christ also!

TITUS

Titus 1---No references to the Second Coming!
Titus 2:13
   Looking for that blessed hope, and the glorious appearing of the great God and our Savior, Jesus Christ!

This is certainly a statement of the blessed hope of our Lord's coming and glorious appearing in the heavens as He comes back again!

Titus 3

No references to the Second Coming in this chapter!

Philemon

No references to the Second Coming!

The fact was observed by Billy that the Second Coming in the Bible is not as prominent as some preachers want to make it. This was not to say the Second Coming of Christ is not important, but some men seem to want to make Bible prophecy and the Second Coming the primary message of their ministry---something Paul never did, though he did clearly speak of the Second Coming, as we have just seen.

Certainly, we are to be diligent and ready for that hour, and we must preach on the subject, but the Second Coming of Christ should not become our major message to the neglect of the many other much needed subjects one will see, as he moves through the Scriptures.

After we closed with prayer, I asked Billy if he had seen Roy or Pastor Sweet, and he said they were still going strong in the Lord. Then I asked about the girl he was interested in, and he just shrugged his shoulders, as if to say, "Who knows?" Or maybe he was saying he just didn't want to comment on that subject. But then he said he was probably finished with girls---till God showed him the right girl for him.

That might have been the best council I could have given him, and I was happy he had come to that decision on his own. He also seemed to have wised up to the fact that not every one, including girls, are who they claim to be, and that seemed now to have made him as skittish as a deer in the forest, who hears a rumbling in the grass.

Chapter 33

I must say I was rejoicing on our way home that we had learned of Billy's growth and maturity, when it came to the young ladies. But soon another week had passed and it was time to go to the mountains for our Saturday ritual of travel and teaching and travel home again. But to our surprise, when we got to our meeting place, Mrs. Cardieux's home, Roger (or Mountan Man) was waiting for us there. After the usual greetings, he told us he was leaving Pastor Sweet's church, because Pastor Sweet had been in "cahoots," as he put it, with Billy's uncles to try to take Billy down again. Roger also said that Billy had been teaching him the Bible, because his own pastor said he didn't have time to do so, and when he and Billy began to study together, his pastor got very mad at him. So now Billy had his uncles and Pastor Sweet against him, and they were trying to shut him out of churches. Roger noted that if he hadn't been "saved," he would have gone over and beaten the tar out of each one of them.

On a hunch I asked him if Pastor Sweet was a pilot, and he acknowledged he was. Then, when I told him of our recent scares while flying, he got mad as hops, noting it could have been and must have been Pastor Sweet, who messed with the plane, because he also had done a lot of mechanical work on airplanes. I thought to myself, that sure explained some things concerning the flying problems, but had Pastor Sweet really meant to kill us? And what about the big show he made of being repentant concerning how he had treated us previously---all a sham?

I was glad to get the explanation of these recent events, which had been beyond our understanding, but now it was time to get into our study, and we even asked Brother Roger (Mountain Man---just in case anyone forgets) to study with us this day, even though he would be jumping into the middle of a lengthy study. Our first pursuit of the day was Hebrews---does it mention the Second Coming in any chapter? And one might suppose that it would take the whole of our study time to cover the material---but not so.

HEBREWS

Hebrews 1---No reference to the Second Coming of Christ!
Hebrews 2---No reference to the Second Coming of Christ!
Hebrews 3---No reference to the Second Coming of Christ!
Hebrews 4---No reference to the Second Coming of Christ!
Hebrews 5---No reference to the Second Coming of Christ!
Hebrews 6---No reference to the Second Coming of Christ!
Hebrews 7---No reference to the Second Coming of Christ!
Hebrews 8---No reference to the Second Coming of Christ!
Hebrews 9---No reference to the Second Coming of Christ!
Hebrews 10--No reference to the Second Coming of Christ!
Hebrews 11--No reference to the Second Coming of Christ!
Hebrews 12--No reference to the Second Coming of Christ!
Hebrews 13--No reference to the Second Coming of Christ!

I had assigned several chapters to each of us, including Dink, Billy and myself, and each one's responsibility was to to see if there were any references in their assigned chapters to the Second Coming of Christ. The above notations show the end of our pursuit---no references to the Second Coming of Christ in the book of Hebrews---not even one. I told them further that the result of no references in Hebrews to the Second Coming was understandable in light of the fact it was written to a group of New Testament Jews who had professed faith in Christ, but were now thinking of going back to their old Judaism, and that is what consumes the presentations and arguments of the author in the book of Hebrews. Having spent much time on Hebrews and having struck out on Hebrews concerning

Christ's Second coming, as far as we could find, I suggested that we look next at James.

JAMES

James 1---No reference to the Second Coming of Christ!
James 2---No reference to the Second Coming of Christ!
James 3---No reference to the Second Coming of Christ!
James 4---No reference to the Second Coming of Christ!
James 5---James 5:7-8

7 Be ye patient therefore, brethren, unto <u>the coming of the Lord</u>. Behold, the husbandman (farmer) waiteth for the precious fruit of the earth, and hath long patience for it, until he receives the early and latter rain. 8 Be ye also patient, establish your hearts, for the coming of the Lord draws near.

The "coming of the Lord" here seems to be something positive and beneficial to God's people, therefore, it appears to be speaking of the Second Coming of Christ and not the Fall of Jerusalem! Some might think that the phrase, "for the coming of the Lord draws near" might favor the fall of Jerusalem, as would the date of the writing of the book of James (45-50 AD). But we are told elsewhere in Scripture that a thousand years is as one day to the Lord and one day as a thousand years. Which is to say that time factors in Scripture or even in human history are short in comparison with God's timetable of eternity.

In light of the fact that our study had taken a longer period of time than these notes might appear, the reader should understand that I had not given them these notes. Rather, I gave each one of them several chapters of Scripture, and it was their duty to read those chapters,

155

seeking to determine if there were references to the Second Coming of Christ. Then when they had done their study, we came together to discuss the implications of what was contained in these chapters concerning the Second Coming. Even the fact Hebrews had not one single reference to the Second Coming was significant, and we had to note the reasons why it did not. Believe it or not, we went overtime, because we took so long and their interest and surprise was so high---Hebrews had no references to the Second Coming, while the small book of James did.

As we flew home, Dink and I discussed several things we had learned on this trip, besides references to the Second Coming of Christ. We had learned further that Billy was keeping his vow to wait on God for any future relationship with girls. And we had learned that Roger (Mountain Man) was real in his profession of faith, while his pastor, Rev. Sweet was not. And we had learned that Pastor Sweet was now working with Billy's uncles in their scheme and plans to try to get some of Billy's money. And we had learned that Pastor Sweet worked on plane engines and might have been the one who tampered with our plane.

So there was much to praise the Lord for concerning the impact of our ministry of the Word of God. But it is true, that where the Lord works, the enemy is there also. And though we did not know it---the worst was yet to come, and who could possibly have guessed what that was, as it regarded the plans of the enemy against us all---Billy and Roger and Mrs. Cardieux and Dink and even me. Surely this is why a Christian cannot let down his guard, but he must keep his heart day by day, because it seems the great enemy lurks right around the corner, and we don't sometimes see him until he has hit us with his hardest shot.

Chapter 34

It was Monday morning of the next week that I received a phone call from Billy, and I was somewhat surprised, because he had never called me, that I could remember, during the week between our studies. He was all excited, as he told me that God had opened the door for him to meet Jamey Jameson---the tract girl. She had come with a group from her church to where he was preaching, and afterwards the youth from both churches got together in the church dining hall for some food and fellowship, and believe it or not, she ended up by God's providence sitting right across the table from him! He even took her home after church and got to meet her parents. That was the good news.

I had no sooner put down the phone, than it rang again, and it was the bad news---Mrs. Cardieux was calling to tell me we were being sued by Billy's two uncles and Pastor Sweet. All of us were being sued---me and Dink and Billy and Mrs. Cardieux. They had even tried to get Roger's two girls to join the suit, but Roger talked them out if it. They even had a (supposedly) high-powered lawyer, and they were quite confident that he could win their case for them. To be honest I was convinced that they had no case, but time would tell, for it might depend on the falsehood they could tell on Billy and any of the rest of us. I could hardly wait to see what their accusations were against us.

In the meantime we faced another time of our study, and so on the next Saturday we made our way out to the mountain area and then on to Mrs. Cardieux's house, which gathering found just our usual group present---Dink and I and Billy---and we began with the book of I Peter.

I asked each of them this time, Dink and Billy, to look at the book of I Peter with a rapid surveying of the epistle, in order to determine if any of the chapters of this book mentioned the Second Coming of Christ. When they had finished, we noted the following.

I PETER

Chapter 1---A Possible Reference to the Second Coming!
Verse 13

> Wherefore gird up the loins of your mind, be sober, and hope to the end for the grace that is to be brought unto you at <u>the revelation of Jesus Christ</u>!

> If the revelation of Jesus Christ is speaking of the hour when Christ returns to the earth to raise the dead first and then to catch up to Himself the living believers at the same hour, then this could very well be a reference to the Second Coming of Christ!

Chapter 2---There is no reference to the Second Coming!
Chapter 3---There is no reference to the Second Coming!
Chapter 4---There is no reference to the Second Coming!
Chapter 5---
Verse 4

> And when the chief Shepherd shall appear, ye shall receive a crown of glory that fadeth not away!

> The major future appearance of the Chief Shepherd is surely noted in other passages which speak of the Second Coming of Christ, and so it seems rather clear that this passage refers to the same hour!

II PETER
Chapter 1---
Verse 16

> For we have not followed cunningly devised fables, when we made known unto you <u>the power and coming of our Lord Jesus Christ</u> but we were eyewitnesses of His majesty.

This too certainly seems to be speaking of the Second Coming of Christ---and the proof of His power and coming is the reality of Jesus Christ's majesty, which was seen, as He appeared to Peter and the other apostles on the Mount of Transfiguration, which Peter had never forgotten!

Chapter 2---There is no reference to the Second Coming!

Chapter 3---A Reference to the Second Coming of Christ!

1. Peter is writing to remind his readers of words which were spoken by the prophets and by the commandment of the apostles of the Lord and Savior, Jesus Christ. 1-2

2. Peter notes that there will come in the last days scoffers, who will be walking after their own lusts and questioning <u>the coming of our Lord</u>, saying, Where is the promise of His coming? Since the fathers fell asleep, all things continue as they were from the beginning of creation! 3-4.

3. Peter tells us such men were willingly ignorant that a great flood came by the word of the Lord, whereby the world of that day perished. Obviously, this is speaking of the time of Noah and the great flood which came upon the earth and destroyed all men except Noah and his family! 5-6

4. Peter then says that the heavens and the are earth now kept in store by the same word of God, as they are reserved for the fire of God's day of judgment against ungodly men! 7

5. Peter then gives a statement that is designed to encourage anyone who might be getting impatient with God's time table! Peter reminds us that we must not be ignorant of one thing concerning God's day of final judgment, and that is that one day is with the Lord as a thousand years and a thousand years is as one day, which is telling us not to get impatient as we await the coming of the Lord mentioned in verses 4-8.

6. Plus, Peter reminds us that the Lord is not slack concerning His promise, as some men might think or conclude, as the Second Coming of Christ is delayed! The truth is that God is long-suffering to us, not willing that any should perish, but that all should come to repentance prior to the Lord's coming! (Author's note--- Some may think it is an error to keep speaking of the Lord's coming in this context, when that event is mentioned only one time in these verses, and that is in verse 4. But it is not wrong to keep mentioning the Second Coming when it is the central event of the context!) 9

7. We are then told by Peter that the day of the Lord (which seems in this context to be speaking of the Second Coming and its events---and remember also the previous mentioning of the day of the Lord and our note that it seemed to be speaking of our Lord's Second Coming also) will come as a thief in the night, at which time the heavens shall pass away with a great noise, and the elements shall melt with fervent heat, and the earth and the works that are there shall be burned up! 10

8. In light of all of these facts, it should dictate the manner of persons we ought to be in holy conversation and

godliness, looking for and hasting unto <u>the coming day of God</u>, when the heavens are on fire and will be dissolved and the elements will melt with a fervent heat! 11-12

Again, we would note that we have to take into consideration the context of II Peter 3, which seems to be the end time, when Christ comes at His Second Coming to receive His own unto Himself and to judge this present evil world and make all things new by His power. Thus, being an end-time passage, it is also a Second Coming passage and the passage does mention His coming.

When we finished our study, Mrs. Cardieux came in and wanted to talk about the law suit against us. She wondered if we should make a large money settlement with them (she would pay the settlement fee) with the understanding that no further legal accusations could be brought against us concerning these matters, and that it would be stated this was not any admission of guilt on our part, but just a settlement to close the matter forever. She reminded us that it would save a lot of time and a lot of trouble, especially in Dink and my case, as we would have to come to their area every time the court called and stay at times as long as that part of the suit took to finish. I suggested we pray about it for a few days, which was agreeable to all. When I asked Mrs. Cardieux what the cost would be, she replied probably several million dollars.

I told her I respected her desire to get this over quickly, but at the same time, right is right and wrong is wrong, and we could trust the Lord to give us victory over our enemies through the power of the Holy Spirit and prayer. All agreed and so did she, and so the battle began.

Chapter 35

I must admit that there were several things that had bothered me about Mrs. Cardieux's idea to settle the lawsuit against us from her brothers and Pastor Sweet and whoever else was involved in that mess. First, it was wrong in that it would be taken by them and perhaps by others as a guilty verdict against us, as people would not understand the whole situation. Second, it could bring to Mrs. Cardieux other court cases, if they thought they could get some easy money out of her just by suing her and maybe even us. She might not mind facing a lawsuit, as she could afford a pay-off, but Dink and I could not face such an action in the future from some eager-beaver mountain person or anybody else, who thought we were rich like Mrs. Cardieux.

So I called Mrs. Cardieux after our weekend there, and reassured her that I thought we had made the right decision, and she agreed we were doing the right thing also. Plus, I told her that housing Dink and me and paying our travel by her plane to her area would be much cheaper than several million dollars. Fortunately, it was summer time, and we would not be teaching at the seminary, and thus we were free to go and come to her area as necessary, even all the way to the mountains, and stay awhile if need be. If some court days were piled up on one another, we could stay over with her. She agreed that we had made the right decision, and she was trusting the Lord would give us the victory.

The only problem could be, if the court case was delayed, and the case didn't come up until our fall semester. She said she would speak to the court officials, and explain our situation, and we could probably get it over before summer ended. Plus, we could finish our studies with Billy, if there were some small time lapses between the days in court. Large time lapses would allow us to go home, but during short periods between court days, we could stay over. Thus, it was settled, and all we needed now were the court dates and the Lord's help in the whole matter. All we could do now was pray and wait and keep on teaching week by week, hoping the court date and our study with Billy could end before the summer ended.

Thus, when the next Saturday rolled around, we were on our way to the mountains and without any problems. Soon we were looking at I John and what it might say about our Lord's Second Coming.

I JOHN

1. Chapter 1---No references to the Second Coming!
2. Chapter 2---I John 2:28---
   > And now, little children, abide in Him, that <u>when He shall appear</u>, we may have confidence, and <u>not be ashamed at His coming</u>.

   Christ's appearing clearly is His Second Coming, which is established even more forcefully, when this verse speaks of our "not being ashamed at His coming!"
3. Chapter 3---I John 3:2---
   > Beloved, now are we the sons of God, and it doth not yet appear what we shall be: but we know that, <u>when He shall appear</u>, we shall be like him, for we shall see Him as He is.

   Again it seems clear that this is a reference to the Second Coming of Christ, because it speaks of a time when Christ shall appear and we shall be like Him and will see Him as He is. All three of those phrases speak of that hour. He shall appear to us at that hour of the Second Coming! We shall be like Him at His Second Coming. And we shall see Him as He is at His Second Coming. This did not take place at the fall of Jerusalem.

163

Thus, this verse can speak of no other hour than
the hour of Christ's Second Coming!
4. Chapter 4---No references to the Second Coming!
5. Chapter 5---No references to the Second Coming!

II JOHN
No references to the Second Coming!

III John
No references to the Second Coming!

JUDE

Verses 14-16
1. Enoch, the seventh from Adam, prophesied, saying,
   Behold, <u>the Lord cometh</u> with ten thousands of
   His saints---this surely is a reference to Christ's
   Second Coming also! 14
2. The Lord comes to execute judgment upon all and
   to convince all that are ungodly among men of
   their ungodly deeds which they have ungodly
   committed, along with the harsh speeches which
   ungodly sinners have spoken against God! 15
3. The Lord comes to bring judgment on the wicked
   murmurers and complainers, who walk after
   their own lusts, and their mouths speak great
   swelling words, exalting men they admire so
   they can gain advantage for themselves! 16

   Thus we see in these verses---
   the reality of our Lord's coming!
   the saints accompany Him when He comes--
   to judge men---which surely speaks also
   of the fact He is coming for us before He
   comes to judge the world!

He comes to convince the ungodly
   of their ungodly deeds!
He comes to judge---
   the murmurers and complainers!
   those walking after their own lusts!
   those speaking swelling words vs God!
   the exaltation of men above God!
Surely this is an undeniable verse which speaks of our
   Lord's Second Coming!

After some serious and helpful discussion, we closed our study and headed for the airport again. But then in a small town a policeman with a very snarly attitude stopped us and gave our driver a ticket. I couldn't help but wonder if this was the beginning of various kinds of harassment, leading up to the judgment of the lawsuit, which had been filed against us. Of course, Mrs. Cardieux paid for it, but the police officer tried to humiliate us as much as he could, as we even had to get out of the car and be frisked by him and even demeaned by him with his smart-aleck attitude and demeaning words.

He finally let us go, but before we left he hinted the need to give him a bribe of some kind. We played the "dummies" game, as if we didn't understand what he meant, but that made him all the madder at us. But he did not get a dime out of us. But we were a little late getting to the airport, which made us late also getting home that night, but at least we did get home safely, in spite of our mountain policeman.

Thus, we had to conclude that the next few weeks, we would not only have the travel and teaching, but maybe even the harassment of the lawsuit and the police in that one little town. But we told ourselves we should expect that, as we were engaged in spiritual warfare, but Christ would win the final battle.

Chapter 36

It was the next week that we received word of the lawsuit, which had been brought against us, and we were to be present at the county court house in that mountain area on Thursday morning of this week at 9:00 AM. This meant Dink and I would need to fly up there on Wednesday, and who knows then how long we might be there. I only hoped that we had a judge who saw through Billy's brothers and their tom-foolery. We had found out that the courts did not meet in this county on Saturday, so we could still have our study that day, and then fly home, unless the case carried over into early Monday. Thus, in order to be there on Thursday morning, we had to fly up on Wednesday, which we did.

As the court convened, the lawsuit against us was read, and it consisted of the following statements---

1. The defendants were Mrs. Cardieux, Dink and me.

2. We were the key participants in the breaking of a verbal contract between Billy Hill and his two uncles!

3. We also were the key factors in Billy Hill stealing the written contract which had been the key document concerning their involvement as overseers of his preaching ministry!

4. We also had taken Billy Hill and were in the process of ruining his ministry by changing his entire ability to communicate any longer with the people of his home community!

The lawsuit was for three million dollars in light of the fact that Billy Hill had taken away their means of revenue after seven years of their sacrificing their time and money to teach and nurture him in the ministry.

When I heard the reading of these supposed contracts, the supposed verbal and written contracts, of which they had no original copies nor signatures, I wondered how they could prove such contracts ever existed? It seemed the uncles could state their views, but could not possibly prove they ever had such agreements or documents. How do you prove there was or wasn't a verbal contract or a legal contract, unless one has a copy or has made a false copy with forged signatures ?

It didn't take the judge long to see through their scheme, and that they had little or no evidence, except their own cronies. And then when they tried to present a copy of the contract, which they just supposedly happened to find over the lunch break, it didn't take the judge long again to see that Billy's supposed signature was not his signature, but a very bad forgery, which then brought the judge's wrath down upon them, and the dismissal of their case, along with a number of days in jail for their attempted forgery. Talk about stupidity and ignorance. Plus, again, the judge told them to stay away from Billy and his ministry, because there was no contract, and further harassment would bring them further days in jail---maybe even years.

Mrs. Cardieux's lawyer had done a good job, and we thanked him for his help. He thanked us for working with Billy, so he could grow in the ministry. He said his father was a minister and he had spent years trying to communicate and work with the mountain pastors to try to get them deeper in the Word of God.

So what could have been days turned into a few hours, and the Lord was good to give us the victory. And our enemies even had a command from the judge to leave us alone or they would end up with more jail time. Victory!

Chapter 37

With all the tom-foolery with Billy's uncles gone, we were free again to concentrate on our studies with Billy. At our next weekly meeting, Billy was late, but came in apologizing profusely, telling us that he would explain all at the end of our study. But he had such a positive demeanor and smile on his face, I asked him to share with us the reason for his lateness, if it was a very good and positive reason. And so he agreed with a smile. And when we heard the story, we could understand why he was so happy.

As he told it, we all had to not only smile, but even rejoice somewhat with him, because it involved Jamey Jamison---the tract girl. And as he eagerly told us, we found out that he had finally gotten up the nerve to call her and invite her out, and though at first she was a little reluctant, she finally gave in. And according to his telling of the story, they had a great time of fellowship, just talking about the Lord and His Word. When we told him to go slow in their relationship, he assured us they were doing that, and they were going out just once a week, and they were going to study the Word together---and missions.

The only difficult part about it, that I saw, was that Billy said he was thinking about becoming a missionary now, not that there was anything wrong with that. But he seemed to have such a clear calling to be a missionary of sorts to the mountain people of his community. I didn't tell him so, but I would be praying that he would not think that he had some kind of a call to foreign missions, just because a young lady friend might have such a call. He had, so it seemed, a clear call to preach to the mountain people, and it would be wrong for him to become a foreign missionary on the basis of a young woman's call to the mission field.

With that information and those thoughts in my mind, I called our session together, so we could see what the book of Revelation might have to say about the Second Coming of Christ---a very difficult book, but we would give it our best shot, as difficult as it might be and in light of the differences of opinion there were on the book.

Some of our day see Revelation to be a book written early in the history of the church, before the fall of Jerusalem in 70 AD, and they would take the destruction of Jerusalem to be the hour of the Second Coming of Christ, which would mean the book of Revelation would have been written before that hour and not later around 90 AD. Others would see the book of Revelation written around 90 AD, and thus the Second Coming of Christ would be in the future and not already fulfilled. Obviously, the time of the writing of the book of Revelation would determine something of the message of the book, as to whom it was written and what the book was saying overall.

I told them that it could hardly be our place at this moment to solve all the problems concerning the time of the writing of the book of Revelation, but it does seem to this writer that the Second Coming of Christ is mentioned in Revelation 19, and it is still future, as that chapter says---

I   What Takes Place Just Prior to Our Lord's Coming!

Verse 1
     John has already seen many things---but after
          seeing these things---a great voice of many
          people who are in heaven speaks out and says---
               Alleluia!
               Salvation and glory and honor and power
                    unto the Lord our God!
     So there is great praise unto Christ in heaven
          at this hour as John sees the future!
Verse 2
     Praise from those in heaven to Christ continues---

For true and righteous are His judgments!
He has judged the great whore, who corrupted
the earth with her fornication and He has
avenged the blood of His servants at her hand!
Verse 3
And again they (those in heaven) said, Alleluia, and
the smoke of the great religious whore rose up
forever and ever!
Verse 4
And the four and twenty elders and the four beasts
fell down and worshiped God that sat
on the throne saying, Amen---Alleluia!
Verse 5
And a voice came out of the throne saying---
Praise our God, all ye His servants
and ye that fear Him both small and great!
Verse 6-7
And I (John) heard as it were
the voice of a great multitude
and as the voice of many waters,
and as the voice of mighty thunderings saying---
Alleluia: for the Lord God omnipotent reigneth!
Let us be glad and rejoice, and give honor to Him:
for the marriage of the Lamb is come
and His wife has made herself ready!
Verse 8
And to her (Christ's bride---the church) was granted
that she should be arrayed in fine linen, clean and
white: for fine linen is the righteousness of saints!
Verse 9
And he saith unto John, Write, Blessed are they who
are called unto the marriage supper of the Lamb!
And he saith unto John again---
These are the true sayings of God!

Verse 10

John fell at the messenger's feet to worship him---
    but the messenger told John not to worship him
        for he is only a fellow servant and a brother
            to those having the testimony of Christ!!
So thus far John has seen a special moment in heaven---
    a time of praise to God and Christ!
    a time of worship as men fall to worship Him!
    a time when the marriage supper of the Lamb
        is announced!
    a time when John is so smitten that he bows
        to worship the messenger---but is told not
            to do so---for he is only a servant!
Thus this is what will take place in heaven
    just before the return of Christ!

II What Takes Place at the Hour of Christ's Coming!

Verse 11

John saw heaven opened and he saw a white horse!
John saw one sitting on the white horse---
    Who is called Faithful and True (the LJC)!
    Who comes in righteousness!
    Who comes to judge and make war!
Verse 12

Christ is further described---
    His eyes were as a flame of fire!
    He had on His head many crowns!
    He had a name written that no one knew---
        but He Himself!
Verse 13-14

He was clothed with a vesture dipped in blood!
His name is called The Word of God!
He is followed by the armies of heaven on white
    horses and wearing linen white and clean!

171

Verse 15

    He smites the nations with a sharp sword
        which comes out of His mouth!
    He will rule with a rod of iron!
    He treads the wine press of the fierceness
        of the wrath of Almighty God!

Verse 16

    He has on His vesture and on His thighs a name
        written which says---
            KING OF KINGS AND LORD OF LORDS!

Verse 17-18

    John then saw an angel standing in the sun crying
        with a loud voice speaking to all the fowls
            that fly in the midst of heaven---
                Come and gather yourselves together
                    to the supper of the great God!
                That you might eat the flesh
                    of kings!
                    of captains!
                    of mighty men!
                    of horses!
                    of them that sit upon the horses!
                    of all men!
                    of men both free and bond!
                    of men small and great!

Verse 19

    John then saw the beast---the Antichrist---
        and the kings of the earth!
        and the armies of the earth!
    they were all gathered to make war against Christ--
        the one Who sat upon the the horse---
            and His armies were with Him!

Verse 20

    the beast was taken!

the false prophet who wrought miracles was taken--
this is the one who had deceived those---
who had received the mark of the beast!
who had worshiped his image!
all of these were cast alive into the lake burning
with brimstone!
Verse 21
any who remained---a remnant---were killed
with the sword of Him that sat upon the horse---
the sword that proceeded out of His mouth!
and all the birds were filled with their flesh!

III A Few Further Observations!

1. This certainly appears to be the hour of the Second Coming of our Lord to this earth!

2. This also seems to be the final hour of the coming of our Lord Jesus Christ, to this earth, whereby He brings the final judgment to His enemies at the end time and then something brand new begins!

3. If that be the case, then those who say the Second Coming of Christ took place at the hour of the fall of Jerusalem cannot be correct in their view, for this is not what took place at the fall of Jerusalem! Just take a look at the world and sin and sinners who are still around us today---several thousand years later!

4. Which is to say that there was not a total destruction of the enemies of God at the fall of Jerusalem, nor was there the glorious entrance of all believers into their final state as believers with Christ in eternity!

5. Thus, the conclusion must be, first, that the Second Coming of Christ has not yet taken place, because He has not come in power and great glory to take His final place as King of Kings and Lord of Lords over all things; and secondly the Second Coming of Christ has not taken place, because His final judgement upon a human race that has rejected Him for all these centuries has not taken place either!

We closed with a good discussion of these thoughts, and soon Dink and I were ready to go to the airport. But I could not get out of my mind the possibility that Billy was considering becoming a missionary, maybe just because Jamey Jameson was doing the same---maybe, just so he could marry her. So I pulled Billy aside and tried to warn him of that possibility, and he answered that they were a long ways from talking about marriage. I warned him, nonetheless, about trying to persuade her to leave her missionary call, if their relationship developed, and not for him to do the same with his call and gift of preaching. It may be God had a different calling for each of them.

As I told Dink about my concern and conversation with him, he smiled and said, "Least ya ain't havin' ta squash some relationship he's havin' wid some lost girl---like he was doin' before!" Then I reminded Dink that one could get out of God's will by marrying the wrong person, even if it was one who was a good Christian, if that one interfered with God's call and will in the life of the other person. And maybe it could even be that both individuals could keep the other one from doing the will of God by marriage also.

Then as we traveled home, I thought back to a number of young couples I had known---dedicated Christian couples who had gotten married, who seemed like a perfect fit---but for some reason they found out they were not.

Chapter 38

It was several weeks, even into a month almost, before we could meet again. Really, we were just about finished with our study, but not being there kept us from knowing what was going on in the mountain area. Mrs. Cardieux kept us informed, somewhat, but there is nothing like being there in person and seeing and knowing what is taking place---including Billy's progress in his love life. Hopefully, it had not gotten too advanced in a month's time.

So, finally, when we were able to meet once again, it was with some uncertainty that we traveled, not knowing what we might find had developed in our absence. Mrs. Cardieux met us at the airport, which was something unusual, as she usually had met us as we came to her house. But it became very clear why she had come, for as soon as we stepped off the plane we learned Billy and Jamey were engaged, something I might have expected, but really not this soon. I must admit, I had never known two sweeter kids or more spiritual kids---but I was still plagued by the separate calls to God's service that they seemed to have.

The question now was, what could I say about it, or should I say anything about it, except to give them my blessing? Mrs. Cardieux said they had not set a date for their wedding, but it seemed to be a couple of months away, as she had heard them discuss it once. After a couple of hours of thinking and praying over it, as we waited for our study time, I decided to say nothing negative about it to either of them, but to pray if it was not God's will, that He would convince them of it. I still wondered how one so burdened to preach to the mountain people, and the other, who was so burdened for overseas missions, could or would make a go of it.

But soon my questions had to be put behind me, as our time of study had arrived, and this was going to be a day of review, just to be sure we didn't miss something, as we had gone through our subject previously. Nothing like a good review that puts it all together, even if it takes several study hours.

I THE BOOK OF MATTHEW AND ITS DEALING WITH THE MATTER OF CHRIST AND THE JEWS!

    A. Matthew is the gospel written particularly for the Jews!

    B. Throughout Matthew's gospel Christ is speaking to the Jews and the Jews are battling against Him and His claims to be their Messiah!

    C. If we read Matthew carefully, we will see how Christ begins to turn to the Gentiles, as He also begins to reject the Jews, as they reject Him!

    D. By the time one gets to the end of Matthew, it has become very clear that Christ has turned from the Jews to the Gentiles!

    E. The climax of Christ's rejection of the Jews is when they reject Him by putting Him to death on a cross!

    F. The key chapter of Matthew, which pictures Christ's rejection of the Jews, is the 24th chapter, as seen in the fall of Jerusalem, after Christ has gone back to heaven, when multitudes of Jews are either killed or scattered to other places outside of their holy city and holy land! And with this context, it should be clear that Matthew 24 speaks of the fall of Jerusalem and not the Second Coming of Christ!

176

This summary brought a lot of questions and further questions and understanding of our study of Matthew 24, and even the gospel of Matthew as a whole. I have found it always helpful to review in large chunks of the material, which had been studied in a class, as it allows one to see the big picture of what has been studied.

Jamey had not come with Billy on this night, and that was good, but I had determined not to mention their situation, unless Billy brought it up. And he did. He began to tell us how the two of them were meant for one another, prepared by God, as he stated it. And I smiled and nodded my head. Billy said he just knew this was the will of God, as he had prayed for it so much, he assured us, even though none of us had asked him about it. He kind of reminded me of the saying which notes that uncertainty shows itself by an uncertain attitude of certainty. And that was where Billy seemed to be this night, at least.

Then he opened the door for me to make a comment, which I never would have made, except for his statement! He said he really would rather die than give up Jamey---she was so special. Everyone loved Jamey, and she was loved by every church where he had preached, as she had been going with him to a lot of places. He said he didn't deserve her, and that she was so much more spiritual and ahead of him in the Christian life. He could hardly wait until they were married.

I then asked him if they had ever discussed the matter of their different burdens or callings---hers was foreign missions and his was the mountain people? His answer was no, they were leaving it to God to figure that out! I then asked him, if God only gave us a head with a brain to hang our hats on? Then I suggested they sit down and discuss their different callings before they even thought any further about marriage. He thanked me, but gave no assurance that would ever happen.

177

Chapter 39

We left the mountain area soon after our study, because of other responsibilities back home. But as we traveled, my mind was still on Billy and Jamey. It seemed to me they were headed down a road that might lead either to a difficult marriage or a break-up even before they got married, because of their differences! It would not be Billy, who would change his mind, but it would be Jamey, who would either before or after the marriage come to understand her calling was missions, even foreign missions. And I had to admit that I was very concerned, if and when that ever took place, not as much for Jamey, as I was for Billy, for he seemed to be the more fragile of the two in this matter of their marriage to begin with. And again, for personal reasons, we had to postpone our meeting for study for several weeks. And before that next journey to the mountains, I was quite concerned over what might already have happened to their relationship. And then the phone call came, but it was not from Billy. It was from Mrs. Cardieux, telling us that the wedding was off. Jamey had called it off, because she just could not get rid of her burden for foreign missions, and God's call for her to go to India to serve, as had Amy Carmichael.

I asked Mrs. Cardieux how Billy was taking it, and her reply was, "TERRIBLE!" He had canceled most of his scheduled meetings, saying that he just didn't have the heart to preach any more. She told me that Billy and Jamey were still spending a large amount of time together, but she was afraid that it was making matters worse, as Jamey became more convinced than ever that missions was her call, while Billy became more discouraged than ever, thinking more and more of leaving his preaching ministry for good. As I hung up the phone, I wondered if Billy was trying to lay a guilt trip on Jamey, while she was trying simply to help them both to do the will of God. And then word came that

Billy had left the ministry all together, and now had canceled all of his meetings already booked in the future.

I must say that I was disappointed that Billy had done this, especially without even notifying us or speaking with us about the matter. Then word came that Billy wasn't even going to church---he had quit the Lord completely, as far as his ministry was concerned and maybe even the Christian life! And he had stopped meeting with Jamey, at his request, and she now was very sorrowful that she had ever dated Billy to begin with. But she was still determined to go to India to fulfill God's calling on her life, and she was full speed ahead to do what was necessary to get there and begin her mission work. And, obviously, that was the end of our meeting with Billy for study.

Yet, after talking with Mrs. Cardieaux, I was determined to go to the mountain area anyway and see if we could talk to Billy and to Jamey. And so the next Saturday, we were off to the mountains not to study, but to see if we could help in the mess Billy was now facing. And, in answer to prayer, Billy did meet with us, and we discussed in great depth his whole situation. We tried to show him how he had put a girl before the Lord in his life, as if marrying Jamey was more important than the lost souls around him, and even more important than the great calling and the ministerial gifts and opportunities that God had given him concerning his life and ministry.

And then he began to cry like a baby again---as he realized he had failed his Lord and allowed a young lady, as much as he loved her, to come before his love for his Lord and Savior Jesus Christ. He was a tender hearted boy. By the time we closed, his heart was broken, but his commitment to Christ alone to do His will alone was solidly renewed---he even prayed God would bless Jamey in her life and ministry in India! And he insisted that we continue our study.

Chapter 40

Our next study, which was our final study, was a review of several matters, as we would give a brief summary of the final points we set forth concerning the Second Coming of Christ.

1. We had seen that Matthew 24 did not deal with the Second Coming of Christ, but it set forth the reality of the Fall of Jerusalem!

2. We could not agree with those who saw the Fall of Jerusalem as the Second Coming of Christ, which meant for these there is no Second Coming of Christ to come in the future, as it has now already taken place!

3. We had sought to show that there are numerous passages in the New Testament that speak of the Second Coming of Christ, when Christ will come in His power and great glory to defeat His enemies and to call forth His saints from this earth or out of their graves to meet Him in the air, soul and body, ever to be with our Lord throughout eternity!

4. We had stressed the importance of the context of every passage and chapter, and that we must not seek to read into a passage something which is not there!

5. We then in our closing hour challenged all of us to understand that the matter of Biblical interpretation, such as Bible prophecy, is not as important to us as are the major doctrines of the Bible, such as---
    the Trinity!
    the persons of the Godhead such as---
        the Father, the Son and the Hoy Spirit!

the doctrine of salvation which is by grace through
faith alone in Jesus Christ alone and not
by the works of man!
the sinfulness of man and his need of a Savior!
and other such main doctrines of the Bible!
etc. and etc.

6. We certainly should hold in respect all who hold to the
major doctrines of the Bible But then concerning the
minor doctrines of Scripture, we should agree to dis-
agree in these areas without being disagreeable---
including especially the difficult area of Bible
prophecy!

After we prayed, following a good clear discussion of
the above thoughts, which went much deeper than we could
spell them out here, I cornered Billy and asked him kindly,
how he was doing? A tear came to his eye, as he replied
with a smile, that he was sorry these Bible studies were
coming to a close, as he had learned so much in so many
areas of his life. As he looked back on these past months,
God had taught him so much about himself, about Bible
study, about the Christian life, about girls, about living for
the Lord, and about waiting on the Lord, and doing God's
will---and where does it stop, he said with a question.

He added that he probably never would get married, but
he and Jamey had decided they would keep in touch and
could see each other on her furloughs home. He might even
visit her in India as the years went by. I sensed a maturity I
had never seen in him, no doubt, a maturity that had come
as God had taught him in the whirlwind of the experiences
he had gone through during these days of study and in his
dealing with girls. I thought to myself, he will probably get
married some day, once his broken heart is mended.

Chapter 41

In the years that followed, I tried to make it a habit to keep in touch with Billy and with Jamey and Mrs. Cardieux and Roy. Believe it or not, Roy went to a mountain seminary and became a pastor for a number of years before he died. I always heard from him at Christmas time and other special days of the year, and it was clear that what had begun as a rugged wicked life, had become a godly spiritual mountain man, who loved the Lord Jesus Christ. I couldn't help it, but each time I heard from him I had to thank the Lord for the impact his life was having on the old mountain boys, as he had been one of them. And, again, every time we heard from him or saw him, he was smiling and rejoicing over the two whippings God had given him through Dink, for that was, believe it or not, what had broken him before God.

Mrs. Cardieux lived into her eighties, and she too praised God for what He had done in those days of Bible study in her home. Though she didn't attend the studies, she saw the results of the studies in the lives of Billy and Roy. She never remarried, but sent funds to the school where Roy attended and where we taught, to help train other pastors and young people in the way of the Lord. And every Christmas she sent my family and Dink's family a generous gift, which was deeply appreciated. When she died, Dink and I and Roy and her pastor took part in her funeral. A Learjet (a newer one than we had flown in) carried us to her area for the funeral and then home again afterwards.

Jamey remained in India, where she had planted a mission work in the southern area, and much like her hero Amy Carmichael, she sought to minister to all, but especially the suffering children and wayward girls and others who were homeless, and Mrs. Cardieux supported her generously also!

Billy went on to get a doctorate, as he continued his preaching in the mountain areas. And if one were to go to those mountain areas now, you would find nothing but the highest respect for Billy, as a man, and as a humble man of God, and as a powerful preacher of the Word of God!

And believe it or not, Billy and Jamey kept in touch with one another and their love never waned, even though they were miles apart, and they saw one another only every few years, when Jamey came home on furlough, or as Billy visited Jamey in India. Then, finally, one day they came to see me, and they asked if it would be possible and proper for them to get married, even though they had ministries miles apart, and they would see each other just twice a year or so? Billy would visit her once a year and she would come home to the states once a year. That way they could see each other for several weeks every year. No one else interested them, romantically, but there was still a deep love for one another in their hearts and minds.

I really didn't know how to answer a question like that, and obviously I had never been asked a question quite like that before. And for most people, my answer would have been, NO! But a number of years had passed---way over a decade---since they had been engaged, and since their engagement had been broken. And yet neither one was interested in anyone else. And they still loved one another dearly. Their ministries for the Lord came first, and that is the reason they never married. But they both knew and admitted that they still loved one another and were convinced that seeing one another a few weeks a year, was better than any other relationship they could ever desire!

Plus, if they were married and lived in the United States, Billy would be gone a good bit of the year in his preaching ministry. But now they could take several weeks a year to be with one another and give their full time and attention to one another during each of those weeks, was their thinking. How does one answer a question like that? It would be answered negatively for anyone else! But could it be possible for these two young people, who loved the Lord enough to be separated from one another for His glory for most of the year, make success of a marriage on that base and commitment---especially when there was no interest in anyone else?

I finally told them honestly that my answer would have been no to almost anyone else I knew, but I answered yes to them, because of their strong commitment, first to their Lord and then to their ministries, and lastly to one another, because of their love for one another. Thus, they were married during that week, when Jamey was home on furlough, and they spent a few weeks together, and then she headed back to India, while Billy spent the next months preaching and waiting for his time to visit Jamey in India.

And, again let me say, I would NOT suggest such a marriage to anyone else---but their marriage became one of the strongest I have ever known, because of the centrality of the Lord in their relationship to one another from the very beginning of the time they had known each other.

In my older days I thought often of those weeks of flying and studying with a mountain boy, and of a girl who loved the Lord Jesus so much that she had even asked me if I was saved, not knowing I was a preacher. She even gave me a tract, while everyone else was focused on a fight between Dink and the Mountain Man. One never knows when they minister to someone what God might do with that witness. Billy was taught the word through our ministry. Mountain Man was saved, because God sent us there. Jamey was introduced to a young man, who became her mate, even though she was a missionary on a foreign field. What a mighty God we serve! I could hardly believe it all, as I wept with joy, each time I thought about it all!

A LIST OF RICHBARRY PRESS BOOKS
By Dr. Richard P. Belcher
Richbarry Press, 105 River Wood Drive, Fort Mill, SC 29715
Phone: 803-396-7962   Fax: Same
E-mail: mabelcher@juno.com
Web Site---www.richbarrypress.com

THEOLOGICAL NOVELS

1--A Journey in Grace
2--A Journey in Purity
3--A Journey in Authority
4--A Journey in the Spirit
5--A Journey in Inspiration
6--A Journey in Providence
7--A Journey in Eschatology
8--A Journey in Salvation
9--A Journey in Revival
10--A Journey in Baptism
11--A Journey in Roman Catholicism
12--A Journey in God's Glory
13--A Journey in Faith
14--A Journey in Sovereignty
15--A Journey in Evangelism and Missions
16--A Journey in Christian Heritage
17--A Journey in Heresy
18--A Journey in Dispensationalism
19--A Journey in Baptist History
20--A Journey in Matthew 24

THEOLOGY

1---A Comparison of Dispensationalism and Covenant Theology
2---I Believe in Inerrancy

GREEK HELPS

1---A Practical Approach to the Greek New Testament
2---Diagramming the Greek New Testament
3---Doing an Effective Greek Word Study
4---Doing Textual Criticism in the Greek New Testament

BIBLE STUDY

1---Doing Biblical Exegesis

MINISTRY AND TEACHING HELPS

1---Ministry Helps in Job
2---Ministry Helps in Psalms
3---Ministry Helps in Isaiah
4---Ministry Helps in Amos
5---Ministry Helps in Malachi
6---Ministry Helps in Luke
7---Ministry Helps in John
8---Ministry Helps in Acts
9---Ministry Helps in I Corinthians
10---Ministry Helps in II Corinthians
11---Ministry Helps in Galatians
12---Ministry Helps in Ephesians
13---Ministry Helps in I Thessalonians
14---Ministry Helps II Thessalonians
15---Ministry Hebrews
16---Ministry Helps in James
17---Ministry Helps in I Peter

SERMON HELPS

1---Preaching the Gospel---A Theological Perspective
    And A Personal Method

HISTORICAL STUDIES

1---Seventeenth Century Baptist Confessions of Faith

BOOKS ABOUT A. W. PINK

1---A. W. Pink---Predestination---Pink's View of Predestination
2---A. W. Pink---Born to Write ---A Biography
3---Arthur W. Pink---Letters from Spartanburg 1917-1920
4---Arthur W. Pink---Letters of an Itinerant Preacher 1920-1921

Discount given on the purchase of ten or more books!
See---www.richbarrypress.com---for a fuller description of the books
and prices and how to order any of the books!